THE STARMAN

The Starman

J.K. Williams

The Starman
J.K. Williams

Published by Greyhound Self-Publishing 2020
Malvern, Worcestershire, United Kingdom.

Printed and bound by Aspect Design
89 Newtown Road, Malvern, Worcs. WR14 1PD
United Kingdom
Tel: 01684 561567
E-mail: allan@aspect-design.net
Website: www.aspect-design.net

All Rights Reserved.

Copyright © 2020 J.K. Williams

J.K. Williams has asserted his moral right to be identified as the author of this work.

The right of J.K. Williams to be identified as the author of this work has been asserted in accordance with Section 77 of the Copyright, Designs and Patents Act 1988.

This book is sold subject to the condition that it shall not, by way of trade or otherwise, be lent, resold, hired out or otherwise circulated without the publisher's prior consent in any form of binding or cover other than that in which it is published and without a similar condition including this condition being imposed on the subsequent purchaser.

A copy of this book has been deposited with the British Library Board

Cover illustration © 2020 J.K. Williams
Cover Design Copyright © 2020 Aspect Design

ISBN 978-1-909219-76-2

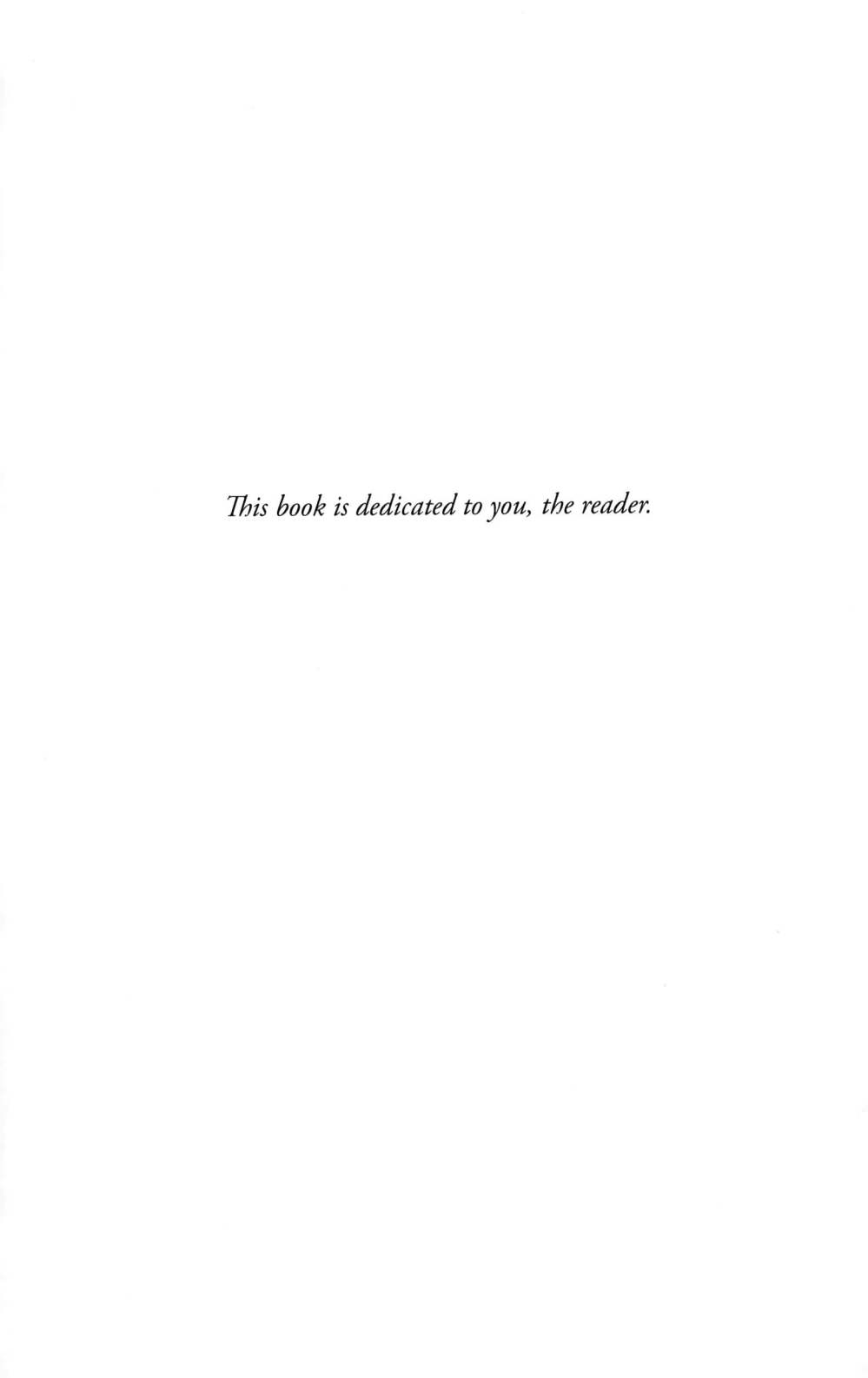

This book is dedicated to you, the reader.

Contents

In the Beginning There Was the End	1
How Would You Explain The World to a Person From Outer Space?	31
Reality Ruined My Dreams	57
Lost in Space	83
Who Cares Wins	126
The lottery Experience	154
Too Many Sad Farewells	187
The Biggest Artwork in the World	230

Chapter One

In the Beginning There Was the End

The door handle was too high for me to reach and I could see the key in the keyhole. I tried to make it open with wishful thinking although, much to my disappointment, that did not work, but I was not moving until the door was opened.

'Do you want to go in the garden, Keythe?' a female voice asked from behind me as she opened the door.

I stood on the step, jumped onto the path, turned right then left past the red brick shed, up the small step, and stopped halfway up the garden path. On the right-hand side was a patch of freshly dug mud, about twelve by eight feet wide. I then looked all around me to see if anyone was looking. There were no signs of life, except for the sound of birdsong and the gentle whisper of the breeze. I took a few steps backwards, then took a short run and jumped into the centre of the mud. I positioned myself to walk clockwise left then right turning round; then going anti-clockwise right to left, forming a figure of eight pattern. Every step I took was slow and I kept checking that I was making the right shape. It had to be smaller on the top of the eight and slightly larger at the bottom. It took a few hours to make the figure clear as the clouds came and went with the passing of the morning. My mind was in a kind of trance-like state.

A couple of hours later, not long after midday and much to my disappointment, I was called inside to have my daily bath. This consisted of a fairly shallow amount of cold water with a cup of *Daz* washing powder and few squirts of thick, liquid bleach. I would be scrubbed with a wooden floor scrubbing brush, as if I was covered in dried gloss paint. This was hard to endure while I tried to sit uncomfortably on the undissolved washing powder in the bottom of the bath. It would often leave my skin very red and sore and I smelt of bleach.

Once bath time was over, I would have a sugar sandwich, after which I could spend the rest of the afternoon in the garden. I had to allow my skin to adjust to the fresh air. This could bring the soreness of the scrubbing down to a bearable level. If this did not work, I would lie down on the cold, stone garden path until my hot, burning skin cooled down, and then return to my mud figure of eight. I followed this same routine for hours on end most days, and was totally engaged whenever I was in the garden.

A couple of weeks later, when the first artwork I had ever done in my life was finished, I thought about how I could improve it. Then, in the mornings I waited by the door to be let into the garden, eager to get out into the bright sunshine to see my number eight. I was so pleased I had followed my intuition to do this. I remember having the idea that I should do something with the patch of land the day before I started it, when I had seen the freshly dug mud. Although to make a large figure of eight just came to me as I jumped to the centre of the patch of land. It was a great feeling, looking at the finished work of art; the depth of the number itself was around four inches and the two centre circles looked like two mud hills. I then spent a considerable amount of time making the number itself smooth. I did this by carefully treading barefoot on any lumps of mud and picking out any stones that I found on my way round. Once it was complete, I remember thinking how amazing it would be if it rained and filled up with the rainwater.

Suddenly, I heard a lady's voice from inside the house.

'Come on in the house now and have something to eat, Keythe, you're going out in the car soon.'

*

The car moved slowly down the hill as the bright sunshine glistened upon the deep blue sea. The turquoise skies blew the gentle sea breeze through the open car windows. The male driver, his female passenger and myself, the three-year-old boy, on the back seat behind the passenger. Suddenly, a large, silver, translucent, slowly pulsating ball appeared to our right, as though it came through a hole in the sky. Just as the driver and passenger leaned forward looking towards the object, questioning what it was, the entire car filled with light made up of many colours. Driver and passenger became instantly motionless and silent and I saw a translucent screen in front of me. It contained shapes and forms that moved at lightning speed. I held out my right hand, palm side up in a combined state of hypnosis and free will. Then I saw a line of many colours move from the screen into the bottom pad of my middle finger. Time stood still; the car was motionless; all that moved was myself and the light of many colours. Then, in a split second, faster than the blink of an eye, the car was moving again. The driver and passenger seemed to have forgotten what just happened. I leaned to my left and looked up into the sky where I could clearly see the translucent silver ball as its perfectly round shape made its slow ascent into the sky. I waved goodbye to the object as, in the blink of an eye, it was gone. I looked towards the driver and then to the passenger, and for a split second I closed my eyes to adjust my focus from the outside sunshine to the shade of the car's interior. Then, at that very moment, I felt as though I was falling out of the sky at great speed, although I had no clear vision of my surroundings. My stomach was registering the vastly increasing turbulence and the ride was becoming scarily bumpy as though I was inside a ball being bounced across the ground. My strong young heart was beating very fast and registered this feeling with my brain. My entire body was confirming alertness and preparing for even stronger turbulence or possible impact, when there was a sudden, yet slow, sliding motion followed by a bumping halt. I leaned my head back and breathed a sigh of relief in what felt like a very soft body-shaped chair. Then I looked to my left and, as though exiting a small black room I stumbled, with weak, shaky legs, into a field of darkness. All around me, rain was beating down, accompanied by very heavy thunder and lightning. This lit up the area sufficiently for me to spot a long row of trees with a church spire appearing on a sloping hill in front of me. I looked back in the opposite direction and saw a river moving very fast, hammered by the rain. Although, I was completely soaked through, the rain provided me with great amounts of oxygen and energy. I fought my way up the slippery, sloping field, falling on occasions and having to dig my hands into the muddy ground to stop myself from slipping back down the hill. The thunder became increasingly louder as I made it to the top of the hill, reaching the gate at the back of the church graveyard. I opened it with a sigh of great relief and the large trees inside gave me some much needed shelter as the downpour continued. Then, as though my life battery had been removed, I was suddenly overcome with sleep. Slumping against one of the tree trunks I fell, unconscious to the ground.

*

On opening my eyes the next morning to early morning sunlight, the dampness of my clothes produced a vapour which I encouraged. I rolled over into its life-giving beam to become dry. I drifted in and out of consciousness until I was dry. Once I was fully awake, I walked through the graveyard to the front of the church and along the two hundred and fifty yard drive. Arriving at a white painted wooden gate, I stopped to look at the beautiful large Georgian house across the road at the end of the drive. I decided to knock on the door and ask them if they could tell me what day it was. I went round to the side door and pulled the cord of the hanging bell. Shortly, an elderly lady answered. I asked if she could help me and she told me to make my way round to the back garden, as she called for her husband. Walking round the side of the house, I entered a large walled garden with beautiful flowers and well-kept beds. The lawn was not too dissimilar to a manicured putting green one might find on a decent golf course.

The lady who had answered the front door appeared from the rear of the house with her husband. They asked me to sit with them at their white-painted cast iron breakfast table and asked if I would like a cup of tea. I accepted, and they began to speak of the terrible storm last night, asking me if I was local to the area, as they had not seen me before. I tried to explain that I was a little confused as to my name or where I was from or what day it was. The elderly couple looked at each other as though they knew more about me than I knew of myself. The conversation then turned to them asking me if I had seen anyone that day.

'No, only you two,' I said. When I asked them why, the lady said that some people had called at the house earlier in the day asking if she had seen any strangers in the area. She said that she had not seen anyone. I became a bit confused at this point, then repeated that I had not seen anyone else today, either.

'Good,' they said, looking at each other before changing the subject. They encouraged me to not worry about anything and to enjoy the cup of tea. The lady then poured herself a second cup after she had offered me more tea and a biscuit. At this point, I told the couple that I thought their home was very beautiful. I turned to look at the house in the mid-morning light of the warm and sunny summer's day. When I turned my head back to look at them, I closed my eyes for a split second, although it felt a lot longer. When I opened my eyes I was in a carry cot, being gently placed on top of a stereogram in the winter darkness. No longer a confused teenager, having tea in the garden of an elderly couple in the middle of a summer's morning, I was now a baby, newborn, watching the dancing shadows of the winter trees, created by the street lights on the windows. I then heard a very quiet, soft, soothing female voice saying something unfamiliar and I felt as though I was floating like a feather in warm air, wrapped in cotton wool, as my mind drifted off down a soft, blue, moonlit, star-filled tunnel to sleep.

It was later that same winter night when I opened my eyes again and could still see the street lights reflecting on the window beside me. The moving shadows of the bare branches blowing in the mild winter breeze outside made it seem as though I was floating. I had no idea what I was looking at then, although I now remember it as if I were back in the room, watching the whole situation unfold. My memory of this is one of the more difficult to access, but no less real.

So it was late November 1960. Suddenly, I sensed a change outside; the mild night was interrupted by the metallic sound of the garden gate being opened, followed by a white light shining on the window. Slowly, the light filled my carry-cot and for the first time, I saw its white interior and navy blue outer. Then the light became brighter, shining in towards me, and I closed my eyes for protection. As it went away, I heard someone coming very softly through the back door, through the kitchen and into the front room. I became still at this point then, moments later when I sensed it was safe to open my eyes, I saw orange lights moving from my head to my toes, creating shadows in the carry-cot. I was being carried away into the night, at which point I went into baby sleep mode.

My next memory was of having my nappy changed, lying on the floor in the front room of 32, Hunters Way... my grandmother, Kit's, house. My thought or instinct was to breathe in and hold my stomach in when it was safety-pin time because my memory told me the pin would sometimes prick my stomach. This was the very first self-defence move of my life, using my mind to order my stomach muscles to contract when my eyes saw what was coming.

Most of my early days were spent in that front room, until I was promoted to the back garden, which was great. I learnt how to walk and fall down in that house and garden. The man of the house where I grew up was my Uncle Peter, who loved music, especially Elvis and rock 'n' roll. He taught me how to fight and fall in the front room. He was such a lovely uncle; we had some brilliant fights. Sometimes the dog, Sanilav, who was named after a toilet cleaning powder in a blue plastic bottle, would join in just to add that element of chaos.

I taught the dog how to protect me in the garden by making physical gestures and vocal noises as if I could speak, even though I could not at that point. Whenever Kit sent one of her two daughters to fetch me from the garden into the house, I would look at Sanilav and look at them coming towards me. Then Sanilav would sit next to me, bare her teeth, and start snarling and growling like a wild, rabid dog

'Mum!' they would shout as they walked back inside, 'the dog won't let us bring Keythe into the house!'

Not long after that, Sanilav was put down and buried outside the front of the house, in the flower bed, wrapped in newspaper. I saw the grown-ups carrying out this burial, although they did not see me looking out of the front bedroom window that summer's evening because I was meant to be fast asleep in bed. However, they had woken me up. That was my first confused memory of loss. Sanilav and I had such fun together; neither of us could speak but we could communicate with our minds and physicality, nonetheless. I knew when Sanilav wanted to tell me someone was coming or when to play and when to be serious.

*

Not that long after Sanilav had gone, I woke up in a wooden cot that I did not recognise although, somewhere in my mind, I knew I was upstairs in the front bedroom of 11, Salisbury Road in Peg's (my Mum) and Dad's bedroom. Although I did not know either of them very well at that point, I knew the house. It was night-time and I was between one and two years old. The cot seemed big. Suddenly and quietly, the bedroom door opened, the light was switched on, and someone came into the room.

He was making the 'ssh' noise that grown-ups do when they don't want a baby to make a noise or start crying. He peered at me over the side of the cot, with his greasy, brushed back, black hair and thick, black-rimmed glasses, towering over me, blocking the light from the ceiling. I focused my eyes to be sure of who it was and wondered why he was here.

He reached into the cot and grabbed me with both hands. Then he began to smash me up and down very aggressively against the wooden slats in the bottom of the cot. I could not protect myself, gather my thoughts or tense my body, as my head was bashed so hard against the wood below me, over and over again. Shaking me up then down, my neck left my head behind each time I went up and each time I went down, until suddenly I felt something underneath me break. Then he stopped, put the blanket over me, walked backwards to the bedroom door, switched out the light and shut the door behind him. At that point, I remember my 'being' completely shutting down. My brain registered him leaving the room and I just switched everything off, fading as fast as a switched off light bulb. My brain had previously switched off certain parts of my body (like an aircraft pilot does in an emergency landing) during the attack, as I knew a complete shutdown was imminent when my head was being smashed against the cot.

*

When I woke up afterwards it was daytime again and I was back at Kit's, Peg's mum's house. I felt different and spent a lot of time after that night leaning up against the wall in the front room, most days with a bad headache, although I did not recall the incident clearly until some years later. As the memory became clearer, I questioned certain key people about the incident.

'So what? Why do you want to drag up the past all the time? Anyway, what are you going to do about it?' This was a typical reply; I always received an extremely hostile response, should I ever mention the subject.

Whenever I saw Peg's sister's boyfriend, Dave Higgs, I knew something was not right. Years later, when she wanted to borrow money from me, Peg confessed under pressure that her sister Wendy had told her exactly what had happened and what her boyfriend, Dave Higgs, had done to me. The simple version of events was that Dave had found out that Wendy was seeing Dad that night and wanted to stop them seeing each other for good. Wendy didn't tell anyone it was him at the time, when he had confessed to her that he thought he had killed Robert (Wendy's first child with my Dad, her sister Peg's husband) in the cot that night when she was out with Dad. However, they had taken Robert with them and I had been put there in 11, Salisbury Road unattended because Kit was out working a night shift. Peg was also out that night with Chico. This attack resulted in Wendy being able to continue seeing Dad whenever she wanted because even though Dave Higgs wanted to put an end to their affair, he couldn't – not after his confession to Wendy about what he had done to me. Even when he became her husband some years later, he couldn't risk his secret attack being known. She went on to have two more children with Dad and he could never say a word against it. Whenever they needed an alibi, Wendy would give him the 'Perhaps people should know what you did to Keythe,' look. Threatening to tell everyone kept him quiet and agreeable.

He would oblige every time because Wendy knew his nasty little secret and she controlled him with it for the rest of his life. If Dad had found out, there would have been serious trouble. I am not sure who actually got the blame for my injuries.

I could not speak at the time, so there was no way of me saying. I did not see much of Dave Higgs again for quite a while after that, although he did occasionally call round with Wendy to see Kit. However, whenever this happened I would be put to bed, or in the back garden. After the cot incident there were a lot of big rows at the front door of Kit's house. Every time Dad wanted to see me, Kit would not let him.

Eventually, they all came to an agreement and Dad started paying me regular visits. He later said that the fights at the front door were about him trying to get me back after he found out that Kit had secured custody of me with Peg's help, but without his consent.

On the day of his first visit, I remember being propped up by cushions on the floor of the front room and Kit bringing Dad into the room.

'Keythe, this is your father,' she said.

✳

How my Dad came to England is unclear. Boat? plane? Legally or illegally from Jamaica? When I was old enough, I would ask this question.

'Keat, me fall from sky!' was what he would say whenever we had the *So how did you get here?* conversation.

Peg said that she first met him through a guy she hung out with called Chico, on an American air base somewhere in Oxfordshire in the late fifties.

Now to describe him as different to anyone I have ever met in my life so far, would not do him justice. So, imagine… you are rowing in a small boat down the Amazon and you need a rest in the shade, away from the rays of the jungle sun. You see a sandy area of shore where you can moor the boat, you pull in and secure the boat. You stand still for a moment, close your eyes and hear the chorus of insects, strange bird-song near and far, mixed in with monkeys screaming and howling. Suddenly, you sense there is someone coming towards you through the trees. You open your eyes and wipe the sweat from your forehead with your bandanna. The heat has increased on your motionless body now that you have lost the cooling breeze from the boat gliding through the water. Then, as your hand clears the sweat from your eyes, he is silently standing in front of you in a loin cloth with a spear in one hand and a chill-pipe in the other, blowing smoke from his nose like a human dragon.

He starts talking in a language you have never heard before. As he gets louder and louder, he firmly sticks his spear into the ground as though he is going to start a fight over territory. He is strange, magnetic, scary, funny, beautiful, mystical, magical, futuristic and ancient all rolled into one. Then you notice his hands are oddly shaped… his fingertips are the size of golf balls, making him unable to close his fingers together as he points to the sky, then points to you. Then he suddenly stops and silently waits for you to say something. No matter what you do or say at this point, you are convinced he's sizing you up for the great cooking pot somewhere deep in the jungle.

You are saying your goodbyes to your loved ones in your mind and praying that bad luck does not plague you in the afterlife! Then, when he senses your woe he starts laughing, tilting his head to one side and smiling, encouraging you to join him in this joyous moment of union between you both… that's Dad.

*

I had no concept of what Kit's words, 'Keythe this is your father' really meant. He sat on the red sofa in front of me in his tailor made suit. Then he began talking to me in a language I did not fully understand, except for the odd word here and there. He smiled and laughed a lot, which I liked very much. He was the first person I had met that I felt I could communicate with through my mind, without speech. I had no concept of skin colour, the only thing I could process was how that person made me feel. He made me laugh; so did Peg, later in life, but in a completely different way. He had the strangest hands with fingertips the size of large golf balls. When he touched my hands very gently with two fingers, I felt as though my mind and body were absorbing vast amounts of information. He reassured me to not be afraid and I was not.

'Time's up,' I heard Kit say.

'Me soon come, yeah,' replied Dad.

Then he put both of his hands on me – one on the top of my head and the other on my chest. I felt very warm and went out like a light. When Kit woke me up, Dad had just left but I felt as though I had been gone for a long time, although it was only seconds. My headaches stopped, my body felt restored and stronger than before.

It was a very weird experience, but I was not complaining. I was really looking forward to seeing him again.

*

The next time Dad came to visit was a few weeks later. I was sitting propped up by cushions, again on the floor in front of the red sofa. He came into the room, sat down and started speaking in his way. I responded to his rhythmic vocal tones and facial expressions. It was very different to what I had heard as a baby. He then tried to explain what was going to happen next, as though I could understand. He was rolling a reefer, then he said some sort of prayer and lit it. He puffed the smoke from his nose like a dragon, then he leaned forward, towards me. He cupped his hands over my face like a mask with a hole in it and began to blow the smoke very gently into my face. It did not hurt, and it was not unpleasant; it felt like an ancient medicine. Many years later, Dad told me that he had brought the seeds from his family's farm in Jamaica and grew his plants here in England himself. After all, he had been a farmer in Jamaica and grew vegetables and plants. He said that when Rastas first became the 'underground' thing in Jamaica when he was a young man, they would come to him on the farm and he would give them food because people were not very nice to them at first.

'I loved them a whole heap, yes sir!' Dad would say, when he was recalling it all, back in the day. In the beginning of the movement they were not so readily accepted in Jamaica, although later they became what they are today – a worldwide religious movement.

Dad saw them as 'Family' before the rest of the world had even heard about them so you can imagine how loud he would play all that early Jamaican music. It was wild and he would be dancing all around the room, laughing.

'Keat, when them children, me sell them whole heap a weed so, yes man!' is how Dad would explain it. What he was really saying was that when he drove them to Kingston to sell vegetables from the farm at market, he would also sell weed that he grew on the farm in Westmoreland. Of course, this was also followed by him roaring with laughter and performing a few crazy dance hall steps.

*

Although Dad was born in Jamaica, his father was from Africa and his mother was from South America. I never met my grandparents, but they knew about me from Dad's brother, Keith, who had visited England once when I was a young child. Dad would tell me stories of how his Mum was old fashioned.

She had refused to move out of the wooden house that the family had grown up in when his dad had a brick house built for them to live in. She did eventually move, but only because the wooden house was falling apart.

Dad had travelled a lot around central America, some parts of South America, and a lot of the Caribbean. He would often tell me stories of the wildness of it all and about the magical places he had seen. He said he had met some very strange people living out in the jungles of South America. As a young farmer, he had the money to travel. He would often say, 'I got money.' He was not rich; what he meant was that he knew how to use money and not let it control him.

I looked forward to my visits from Dad. I always felt he tried to communicate with me, even if it was unconventional for the society I was being brought up in at that time. The connection we had was better than the usual baby talk I received at such a young age. The strange languages in which he spoke to me were my foundations of understanding communications on many levels. The emotional exchange between us was the closest thing I ever had to parental love. Some people would be appalled at him and his 'rituals'.

He would just say that when he got to England, he saw that you let your babies and children be subject to the rituals of transport pollution. Subjecting them and their health to the toxic fumes from cars and heavy goods vehicles that were much more dangerous than any kind of rituals he performed. And you paid petrol tax for the privilege of harming your loved one's health and then voted in the next group of 'political gangsters' to do it all over again. He, like many before him, questioned how those who make and enforce the laws should be allowed to make such harmful laws without the people's consent. The bottom line was always the question of *'What gives them the right to pass judgement on what can and can't be consumed from the garden of the Almighty?'*

*

Although, I saw Dad fairly often, I never understood at the time what the role of a parent was meant to be. Parents have always been an alien concept to me, as I had grown up without them in a very unconventional way.

When I was around four years old, I lived at Kit's most of the time, with the odd night here and there spent at Dolly's.

Kit would work nights sometimes and her older kids would be out courting most evenings. She would often get Peg and Wendy to babysit me, so they would bring along their kids with them to Kit's. They would wake me up, then take me downstairs to the kitchen. Then they would make me stand with my back against the door, facing them as they sat at either side of the kitchen table, with their children standing behind them – Peg on one side of the kitchen and Wendy on the other. Then they would say a few insulting things that referred to someone they called 'it,' as they gave me glares of disgust and disdain. I guessed that 'it,' was me. I was often called that name, but as a child of four, I did not really understand. I just knew that what they were saying was not good as their faces were seriously snarling and their vocal tones were always harsh when Kit was not around. When I did not respond to the insults, they were angry, and Peg and Wendy would discuss who was going to fight me first. Either way, it didn't matter to me. I was not going to lose. Peter had taught me very well, so I knew what to do in these situations. Once Peg and Wendy had decided who was going first, they would then whisper to Robert and David. When they all knew, Peg or Wendy would push that person towards me, whilst at the same time they would both start screaming at the tops of their voices.

'Go on! Hit him!' they would scream as if they were at a boxing match. That would be followed by the words, 'Harder! Harder!' as though they wanted to see me in pain.

So rather than hitting back, I would only defend myself from the punches and kicks, hoping they would stop, but knowing full well that it was not going to happen.

When the first one of them got tired, the next frantically delivered instruction would follow.

'Right, swap... your turn. Go on! Hit him!'

At this change over point, I would look left or right for the new incoming attack and quite often, as I did look the other way, I would get a parting punch in the face from the one leaving the fight. This was difficult to avoid and annoying to hear the laughing when it happened, but at least I knew it was coming. This would go on for a while, with them taking it in turns, until Peg and Wendy eventually stopped getting off on it, because neither Robert nor David were able to beat me. When I looked like I was getting tired, they would come at me for the final attack with a two on to one situation.

'Right, both of you now, go on hit him!' This would start with screaming commands from Wendy and Peg.

So now, instead of a tag team, I would have them both raining blows to my head and body from either side. Then my only option was to defend myself to make them stop. This was achieved by feeling the gaps in between the punches and then choosing who to hit first. Mostly, I would choose the one who was hitting the hardest or most frantically. I would set up the punch with my left then do a right punch to their face. If that did not work I would do right, left, hard right. This more often than not put an end to it and the boys would look worriedly at Peg and Wendy, as if to say, 'What now?' as though appealing for help.

Then I would punch the one who wasn't hitting as hard. This defence method usually worked and they would finally stop. Whenever the fights ended, I would be verbally reprimanded by Peg and Wendy, after which I would be made to sit on the kitchen floor in the corner. Then, every so often for the rest of the babysitting evening, I would get kicked by Robert or David at Peg and Wendy's whispered requests. Then they would look at their mothers to check that it was hard enough, then do it again if it hadn't been. Then they would wait to hear their mum's approval – 'Good boy!' I would often be spat at after the extra kicks and this would also make Peg and Wendy laugh. If I said anything it would only make matters worse so I kept quiet, vainly hoping that they would see the error of their ways. To my disappointment, they never ever saw anything wrong in treating 'it,' so badly.

The two on to one situation went on for quite a few more years, until I was around eleven years old. That was when Robert realised I could easily deal with him. I was outside Wendy's house one day when her husband, Dave Higgs, shouted for Robert to come out and hit me. As he came charging towards me at speed, I dropped him like a sack of spuds with one punch. He didn't get up, and I just glared at Dave, who looked shocked. I did say I was sorry to Robert afterwards, and he never crossed me again after that because he knew I would fight back now. David was different; it took years to stop him bullying me.

Needless to say, with me being bullied and Dad being a black Jamaican in England in the fifties and sixties, life was not easy for either of us. Racism was as common as people who wore shoes.

Even though things like this could be hard to deal with, there were times that were good and inspired me, especially when music of any kind was involved. Now music has always played a big part in my life; as soon as I heard the likes of Elvis, Buddy Holly, rock 'n' roll and very loud reggae music at Dad's house, I instantly fell in love with the magical sounds of music.

*

As a child, I would spend my time between two houses – Kit's and Dolly's, who was a friend of Kit's. I would get sent there by Kit to be hidden away from my Dad whenever he talked about taking me home, or whenever she wanted me out of the way. It was the nearest thing to normality I had as a child. On one of my weekends at Dolly's house, her two sons, Rob and Paul, took great delight in showing me an acoustic guitar leaning up against the bedroom wall. It was bigger than me.

'What is it?' I asked.

'It's a guitar,' Rob replied, then he demonstrated to me that it could make a sound by plucking the strings.

'Do you like it?' Paul asked.

'Yes,' I said as I heard the strings fade.

'You touch it Keythe… go on.'

Encouraged, I walked up to it, put my left hand on the body, and plucked the strings with my right hand.

'And again,' they urged.

I was completely enchanted by the sound. I will always remember that moment because it was amazing. I could feel the vibrations of the plucked strings on the body of the guitar. They both told Dolly at the dinner table later that day and I was still thinking how amazing it was.

'Ah, do you like the guitar then, Keythe?' Dolly asked.

I just nodded because sitting at a dinner table only ever happened at Dolly's, so I never spoke when food was being served. When I was young, being hungry, I never wanted words to come between me and the food.

Paul said I loved the guitar and they were all happy for me.

*

I didn't understand how music was made, but that was about to change when I ended up in the same room as a live band. This was the day of my childhood encounter with a drum kit on Saturday 2 July 1966, that changed my life forever and I was hooked in minutes.

I was at my Uncle Peter Jones's wedding reception at The Peartree pub in the room upstairs, in the late afternoon. There was a band playing on the stage and a lot of people chatting and drinking and dancing to the music as people do at wedding receptions. I was walking around between the grown-ups, looking up at them, feeling like I was in the land of the giants.

As a five-year-old, I had never been to a wedding before, and thought I was doing really well, even though I did not have a clue what the day was really all about. It was nice to see my Dad being treated with some respect for a change, as mixed-race marriages were not really fully accepted at that time in history. Dad and Peg suffered a lot of racist bullying, although they would kick off bigtime if anything like that did happen; they did not suffer that kind of thing in silence. It would be nothing for Dad to pull a gun out from nowhere and threaten to shoot you, or for Peg to smash a bottle over someone's head if they made a nasty remark. When push came to shove, it was best to get out of the way, or else. Anyway, there was going to be none of that craziness today, thank goodness.

This was the first time I had ever heard a live band. I think they were doing some covers, mixed with some of their own songs. Suddenly a lady grabbed me.

'Keythe, stay here, we are going to get you up there in a minute,' she said excitedly, pointing to the stage.

The band finished the number they were playing, so I looked up at the lady.

'Now?' I asked.

'No, not yet.'

Then another song finished.

'Now?' I repeated.

'Where are Robert and David?' the lady asked, looking round the room.

By this time I had decided that if I was going to go up there and have my picture taken, then I wanted it to be with the drum kit. The band struck up another song, by which time Robert and David were standing either side of me.

'When?' I asked the lady.

'After this song they will have a break, then you can get up there,' she said, smiling down at me, seeing that I was ready to go.

I followed the song through the verses, links and choruses to the end. I slanted my eyes either side of me at Robert and David to check their positions. Then, exactly as the band struck the last chord of the song, I swung my arms out like wings and pushed both Robert and David backwards, using the motion of this action to propel myself forward and through the maze of people as fast as I could, then up the steps at the side of the stage. I ran straight behind the drums, where someone lifted me up and sat me on the drum seat, then handed me the drumsticks. I sat on the high drum stool facing the crowd with my legs dangling, while Robert and David had their pictures taken holding the guitars. It was at this point I thought, 'What now?' Then I heard the lady who got me up there in the first place.

'Hit the drums, Keythe,' she said.

I looked at the sticks and then at the people who waited, making encouraging noises. Then I hit the snare drum and ride cymbal.

'Again. Do it again,' said the same lady. I looked at all the people who were focused on me and so this time I hit the snare drum, tom-tom, crash cymbal, floor tom, and then the ride a few times. The drum kit made a much louder sound than I was expecting. Suddenly the crowd started clapping and cheering. It was not just the attention from the crowd that got me, it was the amazing sound the instruments made. A few minutes earlier, I had no idea what a drum kit was, but from that moment on my life was changed forever. The next thing I knew, I was being lifted from the drum stool and whisked off to bed while the grown-ups had a 'kid free' wedding reception.

My first experiences of having contact with musical instruments made listening to music all the more enjoyable and now, when I heard records blaring out from Dad's stereogram, I knew that the sounds were of instruments being played.

*

Dad had a factory job during the early sixties, and he had a Corsair car, nice suits and a house – all the things you can buy when you are earning. This brought him a lot of unwanted attention from the local police, who really objected to him, but he did not care. However, he was unaware of the very real dangers of his ignorance in this matter. A black man having children with a white woman was a very much frowned upon thing in certain areas of British society back then, as it was in America at the time. There was no protection against their offspring being verbally and physically abused, and some people happily exploited this fact on a daily basis… a bit like a hobby, if you like. As a child I would very often be attacked in the street or verbally abused by people of all ages. They would stop in the street, stare at me, then call me some nasty name or another and tell me to go home. I would just hope it did not get physical, because I would get into serious trouble if I fought back. When it was two or more people on to one, I would just weigh it up and realise it was easier to be punched in the face or kicked to the ground, usually both. Then have the food you have been sent to the shops to buy thrown into the street – even the Dr. White's sanitary towels ripped apart and left on the ground, just to add insult to injury. To defend myself would mean having the police visit afterwards to warn me that I was on *thin ice* if it happened again, so it really wasn't worth it. They did visit me once and told me I was to *watch it* or they would *sort me out*. This was when a boy hurt his foot kicking me whilst I was on the floor after being pushed down on my way home from the shop. People would say, 'But you're not black?' These days, they say brown is the new black. They are around fifty years too late with that one as far as I can remember and, believe me, I do remember – I remember being scrubbed red raw with washing powder and thick bleach on a regular basis. Such was the shame of mixed race offspring back in the good old days.

As I mentioned, the local police did not like Dad from the start.

He was too flash and he certainly was not scared of them. Then when they heard the Peg and Wendy story, things got pretty crazy. In short the story went like this:

(Peg's recorded version)

> *'I met your father when I was on the run from the law, for stealing coal money that I was meant to pay the coalman.*
>
> *I decided to take it and spend it. I was hanging around with a boy called Chico who introduced us at an American air base in England. It was a dance night. A few days later, I was at a bus stop with your father when the police stopped and questioned me. They asked if I was Gwyneth Jones. I lied and told them I was your father's wife, that my name was Williams not Jones. They went away because your father backed me up. Next thing, we ran off to Gretna Green and stayed at a hotel called Lovers Leap and then got married. We got a few quid for doing a television interview because we were the first mixed race marriage since the Notting Hill riots in the late fifties.*
>
> *We lived in digs in Brixton and David was born in March 1958. The place we lived in was a slum - damp up the walls and rat-infested. One day, when David was two years old, I got a call from my mum and was told to come home urgently. I got someone to look after David and I went to Garden City. When I was walking down Hunters Way, who was walking up the road from the house but Wendy, who was seven months pregnant. When I asked her who the father was, 'Your husband,' is what she said. Well, as I say, I couldn't hit her because she was seven months pregnant, and I was pregnant with you, although I almost lost you that day.*
>
> *When I got home, Mum said, 'Your father found out that*

Wendy is expecting your husband's baby and he hung himself.' To be honest with you, I think he could not stand the shame of it. Anyway, a rumour went round the Garden City that Kit was pregnant by your father, which isn't true.'

If all this was not enough, things got a whole lot worse between Peg, Wendy, and Dad. Wendy gave birth to Robert two weeks after I was born. Then Peg had Maria, then Wendy had Lyn, then Peg had Linda and then Wendy had Carol.

✳

Peg's mum, Kit, had another daughter, ten months after I was born, on 11 September 1961. She was called Ann. We grew up in the same house and shared her birthday. I never knew about birthdays until I was in double digits and I have never had a birthday party, ever. By the time I was five years old, in November 1965, Peg and Wendy had three kids each by Dad to look after. I was living with Kit or Dolly, whom I considered to be my first and second mothers, although I had no idea whatsoever what parents or family were, other than people whom I sort of knew. To me, people were just people. I tried to see the best in everyone. One day I would be at Kit's; the next at Dolly's.

They would often stop Dad from seeing me, which caused a lot of trouble and in the end Dad violently attacked Peg because of this, and because Kit would not let him see me. She had parental control, which meant she could limit his access to me.

I saw Peg in the front garden the morning after, and she certainly did look like she had been in a fight. For some reason, the police did not get involved. However, Peg did a deal with the CID to set Dad up and catch him with drugs. In return, they would make sure Peg and Wendy got housed with their kids.

*

The set up went like this: A young boy of eighteen went round to Dad's at 11, Salisbury Road in the daytime with his fifteen-year-old girlfriend. They had a reefer of cannabis weed from Dad, and they smoked it in his house. When it was half done the girl put it out in the ashtray. Before they left the house, she put the half smoked reefer in her duffel coat pocket, and left with the boy who was known to Dad. Then, when the girl got home, her mother found it in her coat pocket and called the police. The police raided Dad's house but could not find any drugs. They arrested Dad and just before Christmas 1966, he was up in court.

*

Peg was looking for revenge when she took the witness stand:

'This man has made my life hell and he has fathered three children with my sister. As far as I am concerned, you can lock him up and throw away the key,' was part of what she said that day.

With all the evidence heard, the Judge summed up, saying, 'In all my thirty years as a judge, I have never heard a worse case than this.'

He sentenced Dad to a total of eleven years. He was given five years for possession of cannabis, five years for supplying drugs to a minor and one year for using his premises to smoke cannabis.

Dad's defence said he never stood a chance, and that his sentence had already been decided before he set foot inside the courtroom.

Both Peg and Wendy were housed after Dad was behind bars. This was part of the deal Peg had done with the CID, although they had wanted more than just half a reefer. By this time, Wendy was the wife of the first person who had tried to kill me, Dave Higgs. They had married shortly before Dad's imprisonment. The whole story about Dad did the rounds and the police would stop me some years later, when they knew who my Dad was, and search me for drugs. This happened frequently – sometimes twice a day.

The phrase, 'Just like your father!' was something I heard a lot from them and Peg, whenever she or the police had their nasty heads on.

After what had happened with Dad, there was just no way I was getting into all that. But even though I told them they were wasting their time, they kept on stopping me every chance they got. Also, when Dad was in prison, the random racist attacks became increasingly frequent for me, often daily.

I did visit Dad in prison a couple of times, although it was not a very enjoyable situation to be involved in and I think Dad was very uncomfortable exposing his children to these unfortunate circumstances he found himself in.

Being a single mother with three kids to feed before she was twenty-three years old was fairly tough on Peg. Especially when her husband had been living two lives – one with her, and one with her sister and his other three kids. By the time Dad had been put in prison for what he later described to be a sentence of 'eleventeen,' years, and Peg had been given the council house, she was just twenty-six years old.

*

The council house Peg was given was in a bad state. It needed a lot of cleaning, decorating, furnishing and those types of things that cost money when you first move into a house as a single parent. Wendy was able to furnish her house straight away because she had her wages and her husband's.

Peg had to stay at a halfway house with her three young kids and go to work at the *Nabisco* factory to earn money, buying stuff for the house bit by bit. By working every shift she could get, she kitted the place out with wallpaper, carpets, beds, blankets and furniture first. Then for the downstairs she got a sofa, chairs, kitchen table, cooker, plates, and cutlery. All within four months.

On the Friday night, she dropped David, Linda, and Maria at Kit's to stay the night. I got shipped out to Dolly's but I remember seeing them arrive as I was leaving. Peg went up to the house and made some finishing touches before walking down Bessemer Road just as her ten to six night shift at Nabisco was due to start. She put out her cigarette at the factory gate in a very cheerful mood. She was optimistic about the future after all the chaos she had been through – her failed marriage, her father committing suicide, then on top of that, her sister having three kids with her husband, when all the time he had sworn blind they were not seeing each other again after each child was born. Now he is her ex-husband, who she had helped put in prison for drugs.

None of this mattered. She was at a turning point and there was nothing to be gained by dwelling on the negative. She had a fresh, new start that she had worked very hard for and was determined to make the most of. What she could not afford to buy she didn't have, except for a cooker, for which she had borrowed a small amount from a loan shark. That said, loan shark repayments in the late 1960's were nowhere near as long and expensive as they are today.

※

Peg finished her night shift at six a.m. and bought a load of Shredded Wheat products from the discount staff shop at work before leaving. She wanted to fill up her new kitchen cupboards and the stomachs of her children, who were just hours away from living in their new family home up the road. Her plan was simple: drop off the shopping at her new house, go to her mum's, pick up her three kids and then take them to their new home and have their first family weekend together and get everyone settled in.

She turned to walk down the long alleyway at the top of Wood Lane towards the house. It was early dawn and the birds were singing their morning song. As she approached the house, she noticed there were quite a few broken windows and the front door was wide open. The new net curtains were ripped and hanging off the rails. She took a step inside the front door and the smashed window glass crunched under her feet. There was black paint everywhere and racist slogans painted on the walls in large capital letters in every room. Her furniture had been slashed open, someone had urinated over it and on the floor. The kitchen table was broken in half, the doors to the kitchen cupboards were hanging off the hinges. All the plates, cups and saucers had been smashed. The cooker was face down on the floor. It looked like someone had been hitting it with a hammer because it was covered in dents and black paint. There was washing powder and sugar all over the floor, mixed with more thick, black paint. The downstairs bathroom had human faeces in the bath and smeared up the walls. The mirror was smashed. The stair carpet was slashed, and more racist slogans were painted up the walls. The bedrooms fared no better. All the mattresses had been cut open, exposing the springs. All the sheets and bed linen were ripped. The new bedroom carpets had been slashed with such force that there were knife marks in the wooden floorboards. More racist slogans ending in the words 'go home'.

Peg walked back down the stairs, out of the front door and sat on the doorstep. She lit a cigarette, followed by another and then another.

*

Peg was home – in fact, she was only about two miles from the very place where she was born, Brockett Hall in Lemsford, 5 October 1940. She had to spend the next two days over that weekend cleaning it all up, burning all the furniture, carpets, beds, blankets, sheets, curtains and even the defaced wallpaper, in the back garden. When she had finished, her new house was completely gutted and bare. She not only owed money on the cooker that she now didn't have, but she also had to find money for new everything, or have absolutely nothing. For all of Peg's faults, she and her children never deserved this situation. Luckily for her, she decided she was not going to let this setback stop her moving forward. Peg was always a fighter in these situations and she would always become very philosophical when faced with problems. One minute she would be kicking off, and the next she would be laughing about herself kicking off. Then, if she were ever quiet, you could be sure she was going to start speaking any minute and usually she would start with an indignant snarl.

'So what are you trying to tell me, then? That there is no other intelligent life form out there in the cosmos? Because if you are saying that, then we have a very serious problem.'

This was the sort of thing she would say. The fact that you had not said anything and she would speak as though you were midway through a conversation was not a madness thing with Peg, it was her way of saying let's talk about other-worldly things. As her sun sign was Libra, she loved to talk but at times it would be a bit sudden and seem very unbalanced when she made her initial communication. She knew that, though, because if you looked at her with a puzzled frown when she was being provocative, she would not be able to hide her 'let's talk' grin.

Anyway, she sorted out some cheap beds, and sofa and a cooker, then moved herself, her three kids and John, her lodger, in a couple of weeks later. John went from being John the lodger to John the mate, then to John the husband and finally to John the soul mate, meaning divorced. I never went to the wedding – not to be nasty; I wasn't invited. Peg said she had reservations about too many people putting a stop to it. I was pleased for her and John, although I wanted to ask John if he was sure it was what he wanted. I couldn't do that because Peg would have never forgiven me, even though I would only have been having a laugh. I know Peg could have seen the funny side, or start a war about it, so I said nothing except 'Congratulations!'

Chapter Two

How Would You Explain The World to a Person From Outer Space?

When I was nine years old, just days before my tenth birthday on 10 November 1970, Dolly, who had been the most supportive and normal person in my life, died in hospital during a hip operation. This left me feeling very alone. I cried for days after I was told the sad news by Wendy. I lost touch with Dolly's surviving family once she had gone.

Once I had accepted that Dolly was not coming back, I got involved with playing football at my primary school and joined the football team. I also started to absorb more from my education, and my primary school teacher at that time, Mr. Miller, prepared me for my final year of primary education.

It was in my last class of primary school where my mind was set into an everlasting motion of always wanting to know more. That class flicked the special switch that illuminated my heart, mind and soul to search for an answer. I had no idea how to recognise the answer, though, as I did not know at the time what the question was. However, as soon as my last primary school teacher, Mr. Pitkeithly, told the class what the question was, the real adventure began.

Now Mr. Pitkeithly was ex-air force, super strict but very fair. He wanted everyone to learn as much as possible and he was highly focused on his job of developing our young minds. He was a real multi-talented teacher, whose main aim was to enlighten his pupils and prepare them for the move from primary to secondary school. He was very proud of his ancestry which was a mix of English and Russian.

'Don't push your luck with me, sonny, or I will come down on you like a ton of bricks,' was his favourite saying.

Although he scared me in the beginning, he turned out to be the best school teacher I ever had. I learnt more from him in one year than the rest of my education put together. This was not because my secondary education was poor; it was not. After all, most of my teachers were Oxford or Cambridge University graduates, so they knew their subjects very well indeed.

However, Mr. Pitkeithly was different to all of that. He had a great way of getting your attention and that was what made him a brilliant all-round teacher. He engaged his pupils, teaching us all as individuals about things that were interestingly true and useful in real life. All of this was taught at a pace that worked very well for all of us in his class.

Now the big question Mr. Pitkeithly would ask us always began with the words, 'How would you explain…?'

It was always a good exercise for my mind. I remember the very first time he asked us to take ten minutes to consider the question, 'How you would explain the world to a person from outer space?' Then, one by one, he asked each of us to explain to him and the class how we would do it.

As I was on the bottom table of the three in the class, I had to make a good impression when I answered. Straight away, I thought, *How would I explain the world?* Then I thought that I would have to explain it without telling a lie. I would have to say human beings are made by men and women. Humans cannot live without food and water. Women give birth to every human being, who then grows up and builds things. They create good things and bad things which can cause wars that harm other beings. Wars are disagreements. Then what has been created by human beings, including other human beings, get destroyed, and the humans that win the war take over what is left afterwards. They create a new world. We have beautiful things like music, water, flowers, food, sunshine, animals, and nature. People follow things like sport, religion, education, and science. We create history and invent things that we record in books.

When it came to my turn to answer, all I did was try to hold my teacher's attention, which went okay with this particular question, unlike when he asked, 'How would you explain the English language to a person from outer space?' That was not so easy for me to answer. In many ways he taught us things that were way ahead of our comprehension at that age; this was how he helped us to stretch our minds. Although it was my last chance, I had to prepare for secondary school. Luckily, I had reached the stage where I was able to listen and then utilise the knowledge wisely. Following the school motto, *Trust and Fear Not*, I listened, absorbed, and learnt.

All he expected of me was that I pay attention, and do my best at all times. That made it very clear for me and I learnt more from him than I had ever expected to, enjoying every minute of it in the process. Even when he told me off, I learnt something. He taught me like a machine – he was the equivalent of a 'human internet' thirty-five years ahead of its time. If you wanted to know something, you would just ask him. If he thought you did not need to know the answer, he would basically tell you that you would have to wait until you were at a higher level to be able to access that information. This always made sense when he explained why you were not ready; he would say, 'Running before walking causes...?' then he would point at a random pupil and expect them to say, 'Accidents, sir.'

I would often find myself pressing my lips together and trying my best not to laugh because his style of teaching could often be hilarious, although, you had to wait for him to laugh first and he knew that, so he would often look at me knowing full well that I was about to burst out laughing.

The reason for this was because we both knew that some kids, who were brighter than me in the class, thought they could catch him out and it was not possible. He was like a machine and had only one rule: 'Give me your best.'

He taught me classical music, history, art, sports, English, poetry, drama, meditation, orchestra conducting (with our rulers), history of the world, history of war, drawing, spelling, story writing, modern history, ancient history, exercise and

observations. Now we did observations twice a day; fifteen minutes in the morning and fifteen minutes in the afternoon. This comprised of what he called 'visual aids' which were five or six posters he would pin up on the classroom walls. They would contain pictures with written information underneath, covering various topics in depth such as, classical composers, history, wars and battles, kings and queens, artists and art, geography, the planets and space, ancient history and science. We would be expected to read and absorb as much as we could, then every few weeks there would be a 'visual aids test', when he would cover the written information. Then with only the pictures to look at for reference, he would give us ten questions to answer on the subject.

I usually did about average with these tests. My reading skills and memory for this sort of thing was not as good as the others in the class. I was maybe fifth or sixth from the bottom of twenty-two in the class. I was pleased with that because I was not the worst. I was, however, top of the class in conducting classical music with a ruler, every time.

Mr. Pitkeithly took every opportunity to take the class on trips, and we went to the Isle of Wight for a week's holiday, staying in a hotel in Sandown, which was a first for me. We did regular trips to the Royal Opera House, then we visited museums in London to see all the classical art and history.

He started teaching us about Egyptian history and how they had invented so many things that we use today, even though we credit others with these inventions. He explained that they were a mysterious race of people with skills that we are yet to understand. Then he showed us pictures of pyramids and various artworks. The next thing I remember, I was getting on the coach and going to see a very special exhibition of the Pharaoh Tutankhamen in London. We had already seen the Queen of England's crown jewels, which were priceless – the gold and precious stones were very impressive. We had also been on board the Cutty Sark and the Golden Hind.

This exhibition, though, was very special and had a profound effect on me, seeing all these things that were thousands of years old. The mummies were amazingly well preserved and the artworks were unbelievably beautiful. As soon as I saw the mask of Tutankhamen, I believed in art and history in a completely different way. I looked into the eyes and was mesmerised by the perfection of it as a piece of art. The eyes look in slightly different directions and this draws you in. It is truly an amazing work of art. How was such perfection achieved thousands of years ago? The whole mystery of everything ancient began for me on that day in 1972. I did not really know what I was getting into, but when I was being counted back onto the coach to go home, Mr. Pitkeithly said, smiling knowingly, 'I knew you would enjoy that Mr. Williams.'

As we left the museum and the coach driver turned onto the main road to leave London, I sensed that I had experienced something profoundly unique.

∗

At the end of my primary school years when I was eleven years old, Kit left to go on her travels elsewhere. I was meant to go and stay with my mother, Peg, my brother, David, and sisters, Linda and Maria, although this did not sit well with me.

Now things had changed for me overnight but I had no say in the matter, although Peg was meant to be looking after me now and there was nothing I could really do about it. She was receiving family allowance money for me, but I did not want to live with her and so I would sleep rough as often as I could. From the very first night when, after a short time at her house and not happy with being called nasty names by them all, I walked out into a massive storm – a biblical downpour of rain and thunder. Peg came after me but had to turn back because the rain was so heavy. That night I slept in the bushes at the end of Beach Field Road. This happened because she could not control me. I refused to let her control any of my choices. I sorted out a school uniform for my start at secondary school, which I wore for about two months before I ripped it up in November 1972.

I had started secondary school in a very unstable position, living rough, hand to mouth. I got through the first part of winter eating at school. During the colder times I stayed at Pegs occasionally but, more importantly to me, it was unconditional and I could leave if I didn't like it there. Whenever I stayed there I would share David's bedroom with him and John the lodger. I would often wake up in the morning with terrible headaches and my face covered in blood, enough to turn my pillowcase cloudy red.

'You don't need to see a doctor, you're fine; it's nothing to worry about, it's just a nosebleed,' Peg would dismissively say whenever I mentioned it to her, as though everyone woke up covered in blood. Then, along with the awful headaches, bruises began appearing on my face and other parts of my body overnight. This only ever happened when I stayed in David's room at Peg's. Then one night I could not sleep. I was restless, but just kept quiet so that I did not wake David or John.

Suddenly, whack! whack! whack! I was being hit in the face with a book or something. It was David doing this at the side of my bed. I put my hands up to block the blows.

'Stop! Stop it!' I shouted, wondering why on earth he was hitting me.

He dashed back to his bed. 'Shut up and go to sleep,' he said, obviously not wanting me to question him about his attack.

'What was that for?' I asked, not happy with his dismissive tone.

'I don't know what you are talking about, now shut up and go to sleep' he replied, still not admitting he had been caught out.

Whenever I slept near David after that, I had one eye open. My nosebleeds and headaches stopped after that night. He became very dismissive of me in general after that incident and I pretty much forgot about it. I forgave him, although I am not sure why? I have always found it an odd thing to hate anyone, because people should spread love not hate. Those I have come across who have hatred in their hearts never seem to be happy with anything. To me hatred is just wrong and a waste of life, although I was shocked by David attacking me in my sleep and him hoping he would get away with it made it worse for me. My previous experiences with him as a young child when I lived at Kit's should have taught me otherwise. There are some downsides to forgiveness; perhaps it is wise to forgive, but just don't forget or you may have to go through the same bad experience over and over again.

As soon as spring arrived, I started sleeping rough again, because I just didn't feel that welcome at Peg's. We didn't really get on with each other as I had not grown up with them; I knew them, although not that well. We were very different, and they wrongly assumed that I had led a charmed life, being spoilt as a child. I had been brought up by Kit and Dolly for the first eleven years of my life. They took it in turns looking after me, as best they could.

∗

Spring passed, and the summer holidays of 1973 had arrived when Peg offered me a holiday with my brother and two sisters, to try and patch up our differences. I was not keen. However, after a while I agreed to go with David, Linda, and Maria. We were going to stay in Kent with a friend of Peg's, although she didn't say she was not staying there with us until the very last minute. Everyone knew this except me. The person we were going to be staying with, according to Peg, knew my dad. They had supposedly been friends in prison, which was where my dad still was, at that time. What Peg had told me about the friend was not true. The story that he had served five years for manslaughter was not true, either. The truth was he had served five years for theft. His name was Keith Ward, and to say he was a psychopathic, violent racist would be an understatement, and would not even cover half of the issues this man had.

He lived in Kent with his wife, Sandra, and two small kids. The house was a small, three-bedroom terrace, with an outside toilet and a bath in the kitchen at the rear of the house… not exactly what I had in mind for a summer break. Peg did not stay long. After a private chat, she gave him a few quid for food and then left with her sister's husband, Dave Higgs, who had driven us there.

Pretty much within the first hour, Keith started making racist remarks about jungle bunnies and nig-nogs. This was pretty commonly thought of as acceptable talk back then, but when none of us laughed he seemed to take offence. His wife, Sandra, was the complete opposite. She relieved the awkward silences after his racist jokes by telling him to tone it down. He clearly did not like her saying this to him in front of us. Later that evening, we could hear a row between them both and what sounded like him beating her up.

The next morning, she went out to work early as she was a nurse at a local hospital. We all got up and had some porridge and after this, we went outside to the front of the house to play football and hang out with the other kids in the dead-end street.

The weekend came and went, then on the Monday morning, Sandra went off to work early as normal. Now he had a fruit machine in the hallway, near the front door. It could be played with one coin, as it would fall straight through to the paying out tray. That way, you could have as many goes as you liked. We all started playing the fruit machine, taking it in turns. Suddenly, we heard him shouting in the back kitchen, then moving through the back room, banging and crashing around. We instinctively sensed danger and dashed for the front door, but it was locked so we all ran upstairs and hid. I ran into the first bedroom at the top of the stairs and shut the door. Then I looked through the keyhole but could not see him, and everything went quiet. I very quietly opened the bedroom window, to see if I could escape out onto the toilet roof. From there I could jump down onto the garden, then I could run back through the alleyway between the houses and away. It looked easily possible as I had jumped from higher than that in the past. It was still quiet, so I looked through the keyhole again. He was creeping up the stairs on his way towards me so I ran to the window and stepped out onto the roof. He opened the bedroom door, saw what I was doing, gave out a mad scream, and ran downstairs. I jumped the seven feet to the garden, which was enclosed by a high brick wall with high fences either side, so I had to make a run for the alleyway, passing the back-kitchen door. I almost got there before he did, but he grabbed me.

'Gotcha!' he said angrily. He started dragging me backwards through the doorway, with one of his arms around my neck and the other punching my hands away from the door frame. At the same time, he was lifting me off the ground by my neck. Then, when I finally lost my grip of the door frame, he threw me across the kitchen floor, and I bounced off the cast iron bath. The bath was full of water and shitty nappies. My mind was checking my body for injuries for two seconds and he came towards me with both hands, fingers curled like claws. I stood up quickly and he grabbed me, spinning me upside down. Then he lifted me up, holding my legs together with one arm, whilst pushing me head first into the bath. I tried to grab the sides of the bath to pull myself out of it and then he pulled me out, turned me around, and winded me in the process. He slammed me over the side of the bath and started holding my head under the water. I struggled to breathe as he did this, pushing my hands against the bottom of the bath in an effort to get my head out of the water, so that I could take a deep breath. He then grabbed me round my waist, lifting me up in the air as I struggled to try and break free. He turned me around to face him, pushing me backwards into the bath, and forced my head under the water again. I could see the brown shitty water and nappies when I opened my eyes under the water. I managed to get my head above the water and take a breath. He grabbed my left leg, putting my ankle under his arm and snapped it into two. My leg just fell dead, over the side of the bath. He grabbed me by the neck with both hands while I was gasping for breath in a complete state of shock. He threw me from the bath across the room. I bounced off the old cooker on the other side of the kitchen, semi-conscious. I just cut off and played dead, face down on the kitchen floor. He came and stood over me for a second, then calmly walked outside.

When he was outside the front of the house, he told David and the other kids that I had hurt myself when I jumped off the toilet roof, twisting my ankle in the process. At this moment while he was doing this, I pulled myself across the kitchen floor to the next room and onto the studio couch. I remained there soaked and stinking of shitty nappies in shock and pain with a smashed left ankle.

Around three hours later, Sandra came home from work and I heard him tell her that I had twisted my ankle jumping off the toilet roof. She took one look at my ankle.

'He has got to go to hospital now, he's got a broken ankle!' she said angrily, dismissing the explanation that I had sprained it.

We all went to the hospital and my leg was put in a plaster cast. It was very badly broken and to make matters worse, I had to keep still for two full days so that the plaster could set. When we got back from the hospital, Keith put me on the sofa in the front room on my own. The next morning, just after Sandra left for work, he came creeping into the room.

'You keep your mouth shut! Because if you say anything, I will kill you, understand?' he said in a way in which any twelve-year-old would take seriously, with his wild eyes wide open, snarling and spitting when he hissed his threat a matter of inches from my face. When he left the room, I told myself this was not the summer break I had in mind. Little did I know at the time that he and his 'white supremacist' mates would hound me like this over the next thirty-two years. It continued randomly until they either gave up or found themselves dead for one reason or another.

I called David into the front room and gave him twenty-two pence.

'Go to the phone box and ring my uncle Mick,' I told him. 'Just tell him I need him to come and fetch me, as soon as possible,' and to make sure he took me seriously I hinted that David could be next, if he didn't do as I told him.

Two days later, Mick turned up with Peg and we all left together in his van. Peg accepted Keith Ward's version of how I came to have a broken leg and I did not say a word because I just wanted to get into Mick's van. On the journey back to Hertfordshire I fell asleep and did not really engage in any conversation. I knew that when we got back, there would be an issue of where I was going to stay.

'Can I please come and stay with you for the rest of the summer holidays?' I said to Mick, when he was close to Peg's house, and before she could put a spanner in the works.

'Yes,' he immediately replied.

We dropped off Peg and her three kids in Garden City, then went to Mick's in Stevenage. There was no point in telling Peg what had happened because she knew, and she knew that Mick suspected what had happened was not what they had been told. I am fairly certain that is why he said I could go and stay with him, because he knew, and I would be safe there.

Now Mick was married to Peg's younger sister Cathy. They had four children – two each from previous relationships. Cathy had Francesca and Dorinda; Mick had Helen and Stephen. They were great fun to live with and Mick had a four-piece Premier drum kit in the front room. He had also built a massive four-berth cruising boat in his back garden from scratch.

At weekends he would race banger cars with roll bars, doing grass track racing. I got to paint an emblem on the car bonnet for him. Sometimes I would stay behind and not go racing so that I could play the drum kit, which was so cool. Anyway, the summer went by pretty fast, and my leg healed so I went back to school, although the ten-mile cross country cycle ride was a bit much. I did not want to outstay my welcome in Stevenage, so I started sleeping in the woods in Tewin. This was right near my school in Panshanger. I still visited Mick and Cathy at weekends. They were a great support to me, and fully understood how difficult things were for me, having to deal with the Peg situation. They were aware of how much choice I had in the matter and did not judge my decisions. They introduced me to some of their friends. One of them was a really nice bloke called Nicholas Sheffield, and he played a crucial role in my learning how to play musical instruments, because he could play the guitar. He also helped me gain a greater understanding and appreciation of music overall.

Mick had a brother called John, who had a learning disability, which taught me things that would become useful later in life and I would later use this experience to work with people with special needs, specialising in activities and rehabilitation.

Cathy gave me hope for the future and told me that things would get better so long as I stayed out of trouble, which I did. The funny thing was, all the people involved in my upbringing had various sayings, and they would repeat these to me all the time.

'Have the courage of your convictions and don't believe Peg, she is not your mother. If she says it's black, then it's white. Whatever she says, just think the opposite and you will be right,' was what Kit would say about her daughter Peg.

'Keythe, don't believe what Peg and the others tell you because it is not true,' was what Dolly would say to me.

'You have a choice. You do what I tell you to do, or you become a hit man for the Mafia. You don't get into trouble with the law and bring them to my doorstep, or else. If you get a girl pregnant, you marry her and stay with her for the rest of your life,' was what Peg would always say with a smile.

'They did it for the money, Keat. I is your father… ask them who is your mother, them no tell you,' was what Dad would say often.

I guess back then when I was born, you could just put any name on a birth certificate when you registered a newborn baby.

I was past caring about all those things by the time I was a teenager. I had more pressing issues to contend with by then like food, safe shelter and avoiding racist attacks in and out of school, which could be quite intimidating.

*

One summer afternoon, I was sitting in the town centre around midday, waiting for the afternoon cinema show to start. Suddenly, I felt a sharp sting in the middle of my back, followed by another, straight after. I had been shot twice in the back but I thought I had been stung and so I moved away from there and went to join the cinema queue.

Once inside the cinema, I went to sit down and got shot in the bottom by a powerful pellet gun from close range behind me. It really stung. Then I realised these four kids behind me had an air rifle. Before I could walk out, I was shot twice in the back of the head; the first pellet hit the back of my head on the right, and the second penetrated the back of my left ear. I fell onto my knees; my head was ringing and incredibly sore.

I crawled to the end of the row of seats and made a very quick exit from the cinema. I saw the kids with the air rifle four rows behind me, but I was in far too much pain for any kind of confrontation. I had the pellets taken out of my back years later, although my ear still hurts to this day.

These attacks did reach a turning point one day after school, when I was around twelve years old. A boy called Joe Robinson started bullying David in the street and David lost it big-time. He began to strangle him with the string of his duffel bag. Joe fell to the floor, gasping for air, going blue with tears rolling down his face, reaching his hand out towards me. His other hand was desperately trying to loosen the string of the duffel bag as he screamed and cried. David was like someone possessed, dragging the kid across the pavement by his neck.

I watched in horror for a few seconds. However, I did manage to stop David by shouting at him to leave the boy alone, and luckily, he did stop. It was one of those moments that seemed to go on forever, but in reality was maybe not much more than half a minute.

When this story did the rounds, the attacks in the street for no reason calmed a little. It was what these people had been taught by their elders, and believed it to be a perfectly reasonable thing to do.

Not long afterwards, David retaliated against Joe Robinson, who stopped the racist bullying stuff and became a friend of David's. Strange, but true.

✷

In my secondary school there were a couple of teachers who made threats towards me, saying they would see to it that I was put into a care home if I did not conform to the school rules. It seemed that they also enjoyed adding new rules for me, whenever they desired to do so. They had been told and had noted, that I would often turn up around seven a.m. when the caretaker was opening the building in the winter. This was because I would need to sit on the radiators to get warm. They quickly realised I was living rough. It was often the case in the wintertime that I would wake up wet, or covered in frost – or both. Getting onto one of those big old cast iron radiators first thing for an hour or so was the necessary start of most weekdays in the winter for me.

I was never late for school. It was not the best way to live, but when I was young, I felt strong enough to deal with it. Living hand to mouth, not having the same as the other kids at school was not all bad. I never understood why kids would say things like, 'My parents would not let me do that,' because I *was* my parents.

Anyway, I knew trouble was coming. Then, sure enough, the two head teachers who did not like me for whatever reasons, finally called Peg in to school. They insisted on this meeting with Peg and me and themselves to sort out my living arrangements and nonconformity. It was sometimes hard to hide the fact that my feet were dirty. Often, I had not had a bath for quite a while, so whenever I did gym with no plimsolls, it was fairly obvious. This was not always the case; if I had been able to do swimming and have a shower at school, then I wouldn't have minded the PE teacher looking at my feet. When everyone else has clean feet except you, it can be a little bit hard to hide.

So we all sat down for the meeting at a dinner table in the canteen. Peg and I on one side of the table, Mr. Hauge and Mr. Brown facing us in very serious teacher mode. I could tell that they had already held a pre-meeting meeting by the way they were talking, bouncing from one bullet point to the next, reading from the notes they had in front of them. Just to add to the serious tone they wanted to convey, they even did the intimidating peering over their glasses thing as they pointed out all of my faults. I waited for the punchline, which, after they had finished explaining how serious it all was, went like this:

'So, we can contact Social Services and arrange for you to be taken into care.' They said it as though they were clipping my wings because they arrogantly knew best.

'Excuse me, Mr. Hauge and Mr. Brown,' I said at this point, 'may I have a word with Peg outside, please.'

I walked outside with Peg and turned my back to the large glass windows of the canteen so that they couldn't lip read what I was saying. Peg peered over my shoulder, looking at them, looking at us.

'Right then, Peg, this is the deal I am offering you. Every week you get four pounds and twenty pence family allowance for me, and you can have that, okay?' Then I set up the terms of the deal with her. 'All I want you to do for that money to be yours is this, go back in there and say the following: Me and Keythe have sorted it out, and he is going to stop sleeping rough up in Tewin, and move in with me.'

We went back into the canteen and sat down, and Peg said exactly what I had asked her to say. Then with a Peg-style ending, she added, 'So if we are done here, then I am going to go and I don't want to hear any more about this, okay? See you after school, Keythe.'

With that said, she stood up and left, sneering disdainfully down her nose at both teachers. They were left holding their useless notes in their hands, gulping at Peg's sudden change of tone and not sure what had just happened.

She was happy when she walked out of the canteen because she was guaranteed to be two hundred and eighteen pounds and forty pence a year better off. I was happy because I knew they could not get Peg to agree to me going into care now, because she was my legal guardian and she wanted that money. They had zero chance of changing her mind unless they made a counter offer, which was not going to happen. They were not happy, stuttering and muttering to each other in between sending me daggers. Looking flustered, shuffling their papers together, they left the canteen very disappointed and abruptly. They could not do a thing about it, and they knew that I knew that, which really upset them. The plan of putting me into care had failed, thanks to the great UK family allowance. I saved the taxpayer a small fortune in care costs.

∗

Although I thought I had been clever getting Hauge and Brown to back off, they never did stop going at me like a tag team, so

I decided to increase my rebelliousness against the rules. I had already torn up my school uniform and replaced it with flares, platform shoes, velvet jacket, palm tree T-shirt, bangles and beads, so now I also refused to have my hair cut. While the other eleven hundred pupils had to wear a uniform, I just refused to conform and got away with it.

This thought leads me to other memories, such as when the schoolteachers would ask the class, 'Who does not pay for school dinners?' At this point I was the only person to put my hand up for free dinners. Then there was having to avoid talking about my dad being in prison. These are not greatly pleasant memories, but I absolutely loved being at school and my only one regret was not asking Nick Faldo for his old golf clubs when I had the chance.

While this downside to being homeless was occurring, I insisted on increasing my output of poems for all the staff who taught English, as well as a few that did not. I would stop them during lessons or when walking between lessons, changing classrooms. My pitch was very simple.

'Miss,' or 'Sir, I have been asked to give you this.' I would then hand them the poem I had written, 'by…' and then point to the sky, meaning 'someone up there' as I walked off.

Most of the time they would smile or say, 'I liked the last one you gave me,' or 'Well I am in the middle of teaching right now, if you leave it on my desk I will read it later.' Some staff found this highly amusing.

By the time I reached thirteen years old, my friend Stephen Warr's mum, Shirley, could see I was in need of help, so she offered me a cleaning job. It was in a local rivet factory after school, Monday to Friday, 5-7p.m. two pounds forty pence a week. I took the job and it was great to be earning, because now I could buy food and clothes. This gave me my first taste of working and was the best thing that could have happened to me at that time. I badly needed to support myself in whatever way I could. I took great pride in my cleaning skills, mopping floors and hoovering were my favourite things and this is something I still love to do.

*

I had started this job a few months before Dad came out of prison. I got a message from Peg that he was coming to see everyone, and I was expected to be there when he arrived.

I went to Peg's and Dad turned up at around 6 a.m. Less than a minute later, two thugs turned up at Peg's front door, threatening him. He calmly walked out into the front garden, picked up a rolled up towel from under the privet hedge, then produced a gun and told the two thugs that they'd best be leaving, or he would shoot them. They left and took their threats with them.

Peg told Dad that I was being stopped and searched by the police a lot, and he was not happy about this. That same day, he took me over to the local police station and pointed to me when he told the person in charge that he had just come out of prison after serving eight years and if they kept harassing me he would come back, shoot them and serve a life sentence. I am fairly sure they took him seriously, because he was serious, and they didn't arrest him. They did back off a lot after that day.

Dad had served eight years of an eleven year sentence. I was pleased he had come to see us even though he and Peg had divorced under less than favourable circumstances while he was in prison.

Around this time, I heard that a kid at school was selling a small set of drums. The kit consisted of a bass drum, snare, floor tom, hi-hat cymbals, ride cymbal, two cymbal stands and a bass drum pedal. Now I had previously been using my Uncle Mick Walton's Premier drum kit in Stevenage. I had tried to put my desire to play drums away and leave it to those who had a real talent for it. Anyway, the kid was called Adrian Parsons, who said he wanted twenty pounds for the small drum kit. I had ten pounds saved up from my cleaning wages. Dad had called all his children to be there on the day of his release from prison and had us all line up, then he gave us ten pounds each, in one pound notes. So now I had the twenty pounds I needed for the drum kit. We spent the day catching up with Dad and he had a fair few drinks to celebrate his freedom.

Later that day, I went to my friend Shirley's house after cleaning as usual, to listen to music with her son, Stephen, who was a big-time record collector. He took a photograph of me with the pound notes spread over me, while I was lying on a bed, holding the guitar.

The next day, I told Adrian that I had the money to buy the drums from him. So I went to his house after school with a few friends who had agreed to help me carry them a couple of miles up the road to Peg's house. When we got to his house, he came to the door and wanted to see the money, so I showed him the twenty pounds in one pound notes. He gave me the kit bit by bit from the hallway and I passed it to my friends behind me. Then I counted the money out on the floor tom in front of him. By the time I reached fourteen he was happy, then I counted nineteen but did not put it on the drum. He gathered the pound notes up, hurriedly said thanks and shut the door.

I turned to my friends. 'Let's run to the fish and chip shop, I'm buying!'

We ran all the way there, I went in and got as much as I could with a pound. Although I felt bad that I had short changed Adrian by a pound, I knew he had charged me more than he had first said he wanted because he knew I had a job. Originally, he had told people he wanted fifteen pounds, but he knew how much I wanted a drum kit and put the price up.

As I was sharing the fish and chips out between my friends outside the chip shop, Adrian turned up on his bike.

'There was only nineteen pounds, not twenty,' he said, adding that he had checked it a few times.

I could not lie. 'Sorry about that,' I said.

Then we agreed I would pay him the other pound next week when I got paid and sealed the deal by giving him some chips.

'Okay,' he said and ate his chips and left.

Although I did not give him the full price on the day, I felt it was very fair and I did eventually give him the other pound. I had worked very hard for that money. It was a month's wages from cleaning every day after school, plus the ten pounds that Dad had given me. Dad heard about it from his friends and he was very happy about it because he loved music, although he did not play any instruments himself. He was more of an artist. He also had skills in growing food, acquired from his father when growing up on the family farm in Jamaica.

None of his other kids had anything to show for the money he had given them and so the next time he visited he had one of his, 'I am going to teach you a valuable lesson,' moments. This lesson was delivered in between his uncontrollable bouts of laughter. So I lined up again with his other six kids, and Peg's sister Ann. Then he asked each of us to show him what we had bought with the money he had given us last time he visited. I was the last in the line. It soon dawned on them that he was not going to give them more money if they had nothing to show for the money he had previously given them. So they started showing him all sorts of stupid things and saying how much it cost.

He just looked at them. 'Why you lie? Eh?' he said between his laughing.

Then it was my turn and the other kids said it was not fair because I had more money than them to spend on the drum kit. Dad told them they were wrong, which really upset them.

'So Keat – him have drum. So what you want?' he asked me.

'Can I have an amplifier?' I said hopefully.

'Yes, man! How much you want?'

'Twelve pounds,' I replied enthusiastically.

He told me to hold out my hand, and with great delight proceeded to slowly count out the pound notes into my hand, whilst the other children moaned, saying how unfair he was being.

I went straight out and brought the Sound City 15 watt combo amp for my band that I intended to start. Dad was not materialistic or being horrible. He wanted them to value the money he gave them, even though they took everything about him for granted. They had very little respect for him unless he was handing out the pound notes – then and only then, he was their 'Dad'. My relationship with Dad was very different to theirs. We would just look at each other and then, as if we had experienced some crazy form of telepathy, we would start laughing with great joy. Absolutely priceless... we had fun every time we were together.

*

When I sat behind my own drum kit for the first time, I clearly remember thinking to myself, *Wow this is going to be amazing! Now what do I do?* So, I spent every day doing a mixture of playing to records and improvising. I began teaching myself and picking up tips, wherever and from whoever I could. Most of the time I would just go off on one and play a tribal improvisational style, like I was in the jungle in some far-out tribe. I listened to drummers like Buddy Rich, who was the best in my opinion. He said a lot of deep things about music, including how he felt that he was 'still learning and there would always be new things (for him) to learn' at that point when he said that he was considered to be the best drummer in the world. He had a great sense of humour and would often come out with pearls of drumming wisdom with a pinch of comedy. I was influenced by everything I heard musically, although I had no idea how they did it and only ever had one proper drum lesson from Joel Rothman, three years later in 1977. He taught me how to read drum notation, in one lesson. This was a mission I had after reading an article about Phil Collins in which he said how useful learning to read drum music was to him as a drummer. Enough said. I managed to get started with reading drums, thanks to Joel. Even though I could not afford to go more than once, I still follow his wonderful drum tuition through his many brilliant books to this day.

So, through vinyl records, I studied the music of Alice Cooper, Jimi Hendrix, Pink Floyd, Rod Stewart, David Bowie, T.Rex, Stevie Wonder, The Beatles, Santana, Thin Lizzy, Bob Marley, The Rolling Stones, The Who, Led Zeppelin, Genesis, Rush,

Curtis Mayfield, Carol King, Isaac Hayes, Supertramp, Queen, Marvin Gaye, Carly Simon, Billy Cobham, Paul Simon, The Police, Frank Zappa, Little Richard, Barry White, Eric Clapton, Jeff Beck, Bill Haley, Buddy Holly, Marty Wilde, Billy Fury, Bob Dylan, Simon Philips, Lou Reed, Elvis Presley, Stevie Miller, Buddy Rich, Louis Armstrong and Chuck Berry. Then there was all the 50's, 60's and 70's Rock and Roll, Reggae, Pop, Motown, Blues, Disco, Folk, Soul, Funk, Progressive, and then Punk and New-wave brought us some of the greats of today, who are still making inspirational sounds. The list is pretty endless, when you really think about the history of music so far. As a teenager I would go through phases of music on my play list where I would play say, *Walk on the Wild Side* over and over twenty or thirty times. Then I would maybe have *The Dark Side of the Moon* repeating for hours and hours on the record player.

∗

Around this time, I started lending my cleaning wages money to Peg and sometimes I would stay at her house. When the time came to pay me back for what she had borrowed, she would throw me out on the streets again. So, if I saw a plastic bag outside her door that contained the very few possessions I had or, more accurately, the possessions of mine they did not fancy for themselves, then I knew it was time to 'tramp out' for a few months. This would never be remembered by her in the future when she would want to borrow another tenner or whatever. Sometimes she would pay me back. After a while I just said no whenever she asked to borrow my wages, because I worked too hard to get it to just give it away. That did not go down too well but I needed to eat, clothe myself and buy concert tickets.

By this time, I had started to go to music concerts, like Nazareth, Rod Stewart, Elton John, Thin Lizzy, David Bowie and Pink Floyd. A couple of years before I started going to concerts, I had the good fortune of becoming friends with a guy called Nicholas Sheffield. He had helped me when I was first down and out as a young teenager. He bought me clothes when I did not have any, fed me and gave me shelter many times. At one point he took me to a solicitor friend of his called Geoffrey Clapp and tried to adopt me but my Dad, who was in prison at the time, said no.

I learnt a lot from Nicholas. He taught me about the music of Jimi Hendrix and David Bowie, which he played to me constantly. Then Pink Floyd, which is my favourite because it always sounds new to me, every time I hear their beautiful music.

He taught me how to strum a guitar, although it still took me years to be able to pretend I can really play one. My friend, Steve Warr, and I bought our first electric guitar from Nicholas for fifteen pounds when I was twelve… the same guitar I was photographed holding when I was covered in the one pound notes that I used to buy my first drum kit.

I found a photo of me when I was fourteen years old, at the front of the stage at Pink Floyd's 1975 concert in Chryssie Lytton Cobbold's book *Knebworth Rock Festivals*, and in the far distance, Nicholas is sitting in the crowd with about a thousand people between us. I did not know he was there at the time. Then just as Pink Floyd were getting ready to play, he walked across to me through a sea of people who were mostly lying on the ground. How he found me amongst over two hundred thousand people that day, I will never know. The fact is, though, he did, and sat down next to me.

'Hey Keythe! how are you doing? You okay? Listen, you are going to love this next band,' he said.

Before I could say, 'Where did you come from?' he had said farewell and walked off through the sea of people to the side of the stage with his friend.

Pink Floyd came on stage and played all of their new album *Wish You Were Here* then all of *Dark Side of the Moon*. Then for an encore, *Echoes*. Oh, I more than loved it!

*

Some thirty years later, I brought a limited edition (81) recording of the concert from the promoter, Freddie Bannister. Now that was a trip down memory lane. I had forgotten how long they spent tuning everything up. Also, how I was sitting there thinking to myself, *They are not as good live as Nicholas said they would be… maybe it's some new form of music they are doing now?* I had listened to *Dark Side of the Moon* constantly over the previous two years since its release in 1973, although I had not seen them playing live. Then, just as I was going to have a nap, the tuning stopped, and they started playing the opening chords to *Shine on You Crazy Diamond* as the sun set over Knebworth. It was amazing and the quadraphonic sound was brilliant.

Chapter Three

Reality Ruined My Dreams

Around the summer of 1975 I had moved my drums from my camp in the woods to Tewin and it made things easier for us to practice. We did this at the local village hall. We formed the idea for a band in a bus shelter outside a village pub. The members of the band were Philip Summers, lead vocals and lyrics; Ewan McPearson, guitar and music arrangements; Terry Brand, artworks and George Cant, who was our manager, clothes supplier and transport. Then myself, drums, lyrics and musical arrangements.
The name for the band was 'Mainbeam and the Indicators'.

It was Philip's idea – he got it from a book he was reading at the time, and it just sounded right when we were trying to think up a name. We would write songs mostly about people we knew and some of the lyrics were a bit X-rated.

Others were more topical subjects from that time about fascism, voting, unemployment, and other popular themes that were bubbling up in youth culture in England. It was a time of change in music from middle of the road pop to punk rock. As a group we thought we were great, although we were pretty rubbish. We could not play our instruments that well and we certainly did not care if people liked us singing songs about them, so it was a cross between really trying to do something and acting. We had no real idea or experience then as far as being competent in playing and performing, we just tried to make something out of nothing. Like a rudderless ship, we sailed into the world of musical creativity where it was fun first, second and third. It was mainly the three of us on stage. We wrote the songs from the smallest of things, usually after talking with Armin, who was our advisor on all sorts of things we knew nothing about, or after speaking to George, our manager.

It was a time of great change in music; there were tons of bands creating something new. Whenever you read the *Melody Maker* band ads, there were hundreds of people wanting guitar players, bass players, singers, drummers, and managers. It was a great time to be a teenager. George Cant was a Tewin local a few years older than us. However, when his parents were out at work, he would have us miss school and go round to his house to practice or just hang out. We would set up our instruments in his front room then write, play, and record our songs. Anyway, one time he had to go to the train station and pick up this young woman from London, who had wanted to hear us when she was visiting. George left us writing and went to fetch her. When they got back, we had written and recorded, *George Made Love to a Fifteen Stone Lesbian* and a few other songs. Well, we thought the song would cause outrage but no, they both loved it. The bonus of George being our manager was that he had a motorbike and access to a car.

One day, he drove from Woolmer Green to Burnham Green reaching sixty miles per hour at its fastest point in White Horse Lane, with me on the roof, spread-eagled and holding on for dear life. I thought he would stop at the end of the lane but no, he did his favourite risk-taking thing which was going over the crossroads without stopping. Crazy? Foolish? Just young kids making memories? All three, I would have to say.

*

Now George was such a nice bloke and he tried to advise us about things such as ending the songs together, in time. We just thought that was a step too far away from being 'original'. If the truth be known, though, it was because we did not understand what it even meant. Anyway, George would be up and down to London, hanging out with his friends. He would often bring us black bin bags full of punk rock clothes from a designer called Vivienne Westwood, whom he knew. There were all sorts of T-shirts, jumpers, and trousers. They were often made with unusual materials like mohair, tartan, and muslin. They would also have zips all over them and other metal objects. We wore them now and again at our gigs, at the village hall. The gigs were events as far as we were concerned, regardless of our playing skills or if we were any good. The main thing was to have some fun and we did. It would have made a great comedy film.

We did manage to play one London venue, The Roxy in Neal Street, and there were a few people in the audience… four, including the sound man doing the PA. Outside afterwards with our instruments, waiting for our lift, we looked through the black bins and found little square pieces of paper, with agreements typed on them for bands to play at the Roxy. There was one for Dire Straits and The Police to play there. They were getting paid one hundred and twenty pounds, and forty pounds. They were not that famous then but we all know what happened shortly afterwards. Anyway, George kept telling us about this band in London he hung out with, called The Sex Pistols. We just thought it was some new band, like all the others. Then, one Sunday morning, George said he was going to be on a TV programme called, *This Weekend*. We watched it and there was George sitting on a speaker at the side of the stage. The commentator was talking about this new band and their style of music. A little while after that programme, they were on TV again, this time with Bill Grundy – and the rest is history. Well that was it. Not only did we have him banging on about us ending the songs together, but he was also now on the TV, selling out. He had to be fired before he left us for the better band. Once the Punk thing all started to happen, we did not see much of George again. The last time I remember seeing him was when we played our last gig at Tewin village Hall. We spoke before the gig and he was all excited because we had started to end a lot of the songs together, like he had always said we should. He was at the side of the stage doing a double thumbs up with a big smile on his face because he loved how much we had improved. We had gone from being the worst band in England, to not quite the worst band in England!

*

Everything we did or thought about over the next year or so was connected to music for me and most of my friends.

Then, quite suddenly I had arrived at the last year of secondary school sooner than I had wanted. One day, for no real reason, I was called into the office by Mr. Hauge and Mr. Brown. Maybe they wanted poems? No. As I walked into the office, I could tell straight away I was in for trouble and it was not going to be pleasant. You get a feel for these things after a while. Sure enough, they started to tell me that I was a failure and would never amount to anything. I did not respond, because I could tell they wanted me to engage in this, so I just thought to myself, *I am not actually in trouble for anything here, so long as I am careful and keep my mouth shut, I'm good.*

So they continued telling me how I was never going to amount to anything in life. Then there was a pause.

'Okay,' I said, trying to get to the end of this situation.

They did not like me saying that, so they went for their knock-out blow.

'You will end up dead of a drug overdose, in a country lane,' one said, as if he could predict the future.

'Sir, I don't take drugs. I don't even smoke.'

This angered them. 'Get out!' they shouted and pointed to the door. They were annoyed that their attempts to provoke me into a row had not worked out well for them. I don't like being smug, but I did laugh when I left the office because normally I would have said something controversial and got into it with them. That day, though, I took offence and used what they said to me, against them. I knew they would have loved to throw me out of school but could not find a good enough reason. I decided to help them out as a parting gift. I gave the pleasure of my expulsion from school to someone higher than them, the Headmaster.

I had only agreed to take part in two exams, English and Art. The rest of the exams, to me, were mostly heavily invested in 'mind control.' The opinion of certain experts that we must agree with, or you are said to be 'not right in the head' was not for me… indoctrination followed by disappointment and stagnation of the imagination. This was best left for those who voted for that type of education. My disregard for these things was not me being dismissive of very thoughtful or meaningful things. It was because I just did not understand how, for instance, you could dress up the 'slave trade' or the relentless plunder of the Americas, Africa, Asia, India, Australia the Caribbean or the Pacific islands. These actions largely created the wealth of Europe at the expense of other human beings. How was this knowledge of their historical beliefs going to further my knowledge? How was I going to use such information and apply it to life after school? I felt that the history of the world had been largely lost, because what schools were teaching at this time was not a true, unbiased version of history. It was more about justifying the plundering of riches with unreasonable force. The whole thing could have been looked at more intelligently, in my opinion. Using the word 'savages' or 'tribes' to justify what had happened, is not a true account of history. These words were largely used to create a sense of superiority and this resulted in creating a patriotic fever that covered up the dark parts of human history.

※

I managed to keep a fairly low profile until around February 1977. I was sixteen and three months; every month counts at that age. I wanted to get expelled but could not decide how. For some reason I wanted my exit to be original, not the usual fighting, smoking, swearing at the teachers, or breaking stuff. No, it had to be original and dramatic. I wanted to make a 'big statement' that would identify my displeasure at the way I had been bullied by certain teachers. It had to make them realise that I had tolerated a lot of their silliness, even though most of it could have been avoided if I had been willing to conform and done things normally, as they had wanted, but I just could not agree to that kind of subservience.

Ever since I was in primary education, school lunches were my only guaranteed daily meal, and I loved the dinner ladies. On this particular day I had my lunch and, instead of eating as many leftovers as possible as I would normally do, I ate my lunch, and then went to the frozen pond by the physics lab. I smashed out a four inch thick lump of ice, the size of a shoebox. I checked that one of the double doors to the building I was going to drop it from was locked. Then I made my way, with the ice box, to the second floor where my classroom was. I opened the window and waited for the Headmaster to start his dinnertime rounds of the building, with the ice box melting in my hands. Sure enough, he came marching down the quad, bang on time. He was wearing his long black robe and he walked with a rhythm towards the door. I tuned into his walking rhythm. The plan was to drop the block of ice and miss him by around two feet to his right when he reached to open the door to come into the building (the door to his right being locked – I checked). He would use the left-hand door of the two, so this left me a three by four feet slab of pavement on which to land the ice shoebox. With the aid of science, skill, luck, perfect timing and a large helping of stupidity, I dropped the block of ice. It sailed straight down in a plumb line, and then shattered into thousands of pieces as close as I could get it to him without directly hitting him. He jumped, then immediately looked up as I pulled myself in from the open window. I ran downstairs to the first floor and sat down next to a girl called Sharon.

'I've been here talking to you for ten minutes, okay?' I said quickly.

'Yes, okay.'

Seconds later, the Headmaster stormed into the room and scanned the people in it, then pointed at me.

'Williams, with me! Now!' he bellowed. So I followed him upstairs to the room where I had dropped the ice from. He asked me for my shoe which I slipped off and handed to him. He turned it upside down and matched the tread against the dusty footprints by the window, the very place where I had stood waiting for him to join my dramatic exit from school and entry into the real world.

'My office! He marched off, expecting me to follow. Well it certainly looked like it was 'School's out!' time now, and I was so pleased no one was hurt. I followed him into his office,

'I want you to leave the school premises immediately and never return. If you do, the police will be called and I will have you removed. Do I make myself clear?' he said, like a headmaster using his authority.

'Can I come back for my exams?' I asked. 'I am doing English and Art.'

He paused for a moment, looking at me in disbelief.

'Look, Sir, I know it was wrong and I am sorry. But I really want to do the exams?' I said with a 'last request' tone.

'Humph! Yes alright,' he replied testily, 'you can do the exams but other than that, I do not want to see you on the premises in any circumstances, do you understand?'

'Can I come in for my dinners?' I asked hopefully.

'No! You cannot come in for dinners. Now I want you off the premises this minute.'

'Thanks for being a good headmaster, Sir, and I am sorry for what I have done today.'

'Yes, well… I really don't know what to say to you, Mr. Williams, I really don't. Do something with your life, but right now I want you to leave.'

'Okay, thanks. Goodbye then, Sir,' I said as I turned around and left.

Mr. Tregunna was a good headmaster, a big sports enthusiast, but he failed to stop certain teachers picking on me. I had enough problems outside school, without having to deal with any more when I was there. I felt that he either did not know about the bullying I'd had to endure, or he turned a blind eye to it. His proudest Headmaster moment was when Nick Faldo won his first local golf tournament. He gathered the whole school into the hall, and told us all that his first big tournament win was a really great thing. Then he said that Nick was destined for greatness, which was good for us all and the school. He was absolutely right, Nick became a world champion golfer. However, as we all found out pretty quickly on Panshanger golf course, it is not that easy, but that did not stop us going golf crazy, because of his success. It was a funny feeling to think that he was the guy who used to smile at me, being the oddly dressed pupil of the school whenever we passed on the quad… I would be dressed like a glam rock hippie and he would be in his grey suit with his blue prefect badge. Now he was on his way to fame. That gave us all a certain amount of rare optimism for our futures.

*

As I walked out of the school gates on that cold February afternoon, the other pupils were milling around doing lunchtime things. Now I had finally broken free, I had no idea what I was going to do. One might compare my behaviour that day to a person driving a car the wrong way down a one way street that is full of tanks coming the other way. Just for good measure, it was also like me wearing a blindfold and singing happily as I put my foot firmly down on the accelerator towards the oncoming tanks.

Everyone had heard about what I had done and there was talk of me returning for my exams. The possibility of my being arrested if I did anything wrong, was fairly shocking for some pupils. However, when I put the record straight and told the other kids at school I had meant to miss him, they considered the consequences if I had not missed. It never entered my mind that it could have happened that way. Even now I do find it hard to believe that I chose to exit my education in such a way, but I did. With a dramatic bang! Now my advice to anyone who finds themselves in a similar situation would be, don't get in the car or ever wear a blindfold when driving. Make the most of school if you can and learn as much as you can. If you end up having to listen and conform for a few years, it's no big deal because afterwards you can do whatever you like with your life. However, if you waste your education through a self-generated misinformed reality, you will have to teach yourself everything you need to know later in life, just as I have mostly done. Then it's a lot harder, and very time consuming – it can often take a lifetime.

*

Art and English exams day arrived. Art in the morning at ten a.m. then English at twelve, lunchtime in the hall next to the canteen. I had not been in school since February; it was now May.

My Art composition was a painting of a fire in some wood, with the Devil's trident coming out of it towards a coffin, and above the coffin a large cloud with two arms reaching down towards it, entitled 'Heaven or Hell'. At the time, I thought it was great, now I wonder what on earth was I thinking? I should have done a lovely Monet type, countryside thing.

However, I passed my exam, which proved that some qualifications meant you just turned up and painted badly on paper. If only I had turned up at all the other exams.

So once my Art exam was over, I went into my English exam. I walked into the main hall and took a seat in the back row, ten minutes or so before it was meant to start. Mr. Newby (who had taught me English and introduced me to the work of George Orwell, who was his favourite, and then Shakespeare, Keats, and Wordsworth, to name but a few), walked towards me, making his way through the rows of exam desks with a 'glad you came' smile on his face.

He handed me the exam paper. 'Well, Keythe, this is it. Do your best, and I hope to see your name in print someday. Good Luck,' he said optimistically.

'Thank you, Sir,' I replied, grateful for his attempt to boost my confidence.

Before I knew it, the room had filled up with other pupils.

'Turn over your exam papers and you have up to ninety minutes to complete the work. Good luck!' the invigilator said.

I read through the exam paper and did not really understand what I was meant to do. I very quickly decided. It was time for my primary school English question to be answered on this exam paper. This question was, 'How would you explain the world to a person from outer space?'

My answer went along the lines that everything in the world that we call man-made actually begins with a woman creating a man. Without a woman there is no man. However, here on earth there is constant warfare and a person from outer space would be in danger here unless they could change the endless war into the endless peace.

Anyway, I am fairly sure that Mr. Newby ensured I got a pass for my English exam. When I got the pass results for both exams on a green computer-generated slip, I was pleased. The artwork I did for the exam was just a dramatic, emotional response to finding myself homeless in the woods by a camp fire, if I was lucky, or wondering if the descending clouds in the cold nights would carry me away for good.

The English exam piece was something I had been thinking about for around five or six years, ever since Mr. Pitkeithley had asked us the question in one of his, 'How would you explain?' sessions when I was ten years old. Mr. Newby had taught me how to make the extra effort to read things properly and enable myself to understand much more about the English language. It must have been hard for him to teach me because forty-seven years later, I am still confused about it all.

Being educated by Mr. Pitkeithly had left me very influenced by his unfailing enthusiasm and five years later, which almost seemed like a lifetime, I had used his question to answer my English exam. That was the day I learnt that passing an exam and having a 'qualification' to prove it does not always mean that you are clever.

When I walked up and handed in my work to the invigilator, my main thought was not sadness that my education was over at that point; it was, *What am I going to do with my life now?*

✳

I was now one of the unemployed, although I still did a part-time cleaning job. This was now for a different company, thanks to Kit getting me a job at Smith and Nephew, where I was paid six pounds fifty pence a week. I had access to plenty of plasters and bandages if I needed them, because that's what they made. My cleaning wages were not going to be anywhere near enough to live on now that I had left school.

About six weeks passed with me being out of full-time work. I did attend a few job interviews, but was not successful. Then my half-brother, Robert, came to see me and said that he had been sacked from his supermarket warehouse job for helping himself to chocolate bars. He strongly suggested that if I went there and applied for the job, I would definitely get it. I went there the next day and asked to see the person who hired the workforce. Before I could prepare or compose myself for any questions, I was standing in front of the Manager in his office.

'You look remarkably like the last person we had here, whom I sacked for pilfering,' he said in a probing manner.

I am two weeks older than Robert and we have the same father, different mother.

However, I did not expect him to ask whether I knew Robert Jones, so I had to lie.

'No, I do not,' I replied.

'Really? Well, you went to the same school and you were in the same year,' he said continuing his probing.

I had not thought of this coming up in conversation when I filled in the very brief application form before being shown into his office, and so I had to lie again.

'No, sir, I do not know him; he was not in my class,' I answered, hoping that would be the last mention of this matter.

'Well, that's remarkable, because you look so much like him. I swear you could be twins,' he pressed.

At this point, I could feel the job slipping through my fingers.

'Did you say his name was Jones?' I asked.

'Yes, that's right.'

I then took a pause and did a 'down memory lane' stare, followed by a slight shaking of the head.

'No, I don't know him. Anyway, I am Mr. Williams,' I said, shrugging my shoulders, hoping that this acting cameo would help change the subject.

After a short silence, he said, 'Okay. Well when can you start?'

'When would be good for you, Mr. Durrent?' I asked enthusiastically.

We agreed on the following Monday at seven a.m. I walked out and across the road to the record shop, where Robert was waiting for me and I told him the good news.

'Told you so, Keythe,' he said, and then we had a good laugh when I told him what had been said. He told me not to worry about it, and I didn't give it a second thought after that. I finished my cleaning job at Smith and Nephew and started at Fine Fare Supermarket, earning a little bit more – sixteen pounds and forty pence a week – and one of the perks of the job was a cheap canteen. Also, when stock got damaged, I had to throw it away and sometimes it did not make it to the dustbin because my mouth got in the way.

∗

By this time, I was staying with Kit again and her youngest daughter, Ann. I had not seen or heard much from Kit since I was eleven years old, when she had left to go travelling.

I was now sixteen and had been living on and off the streets for five years at this point. It was nice staying in a house again, having a bit of a break from the ups and downs of being homeless. Working every day was a good thing for me and I had soon forgotten all the negatives I had endured by being homeless. Negatives that I had partly created myself through my lack of accepting any kind of parental guidance.

It was not all doom and gloom, though, because by this time I had been playing drums and guitar for five years. Also, I had formed a punk rock band in Tewin two years earlier with some friends. We did continue for a little while after 1977 and got a second guitarist but we drifted apart once we had to commit ourselves to working for a living.

By this time, we had very sadly lost a few really close friends in tragic road accidents… Armin, a really nice kid, who had spent many nights enlightening us about various hip and mysterious things round the campfires… Shirley's eldest son, Gary, who also died very young. He had introduced me to progressive music and called me The Spaceman. He was also the person who taught me how to question the things they aired on television.

Anyway, after our last gig we went our separate ways. By this time I had finished working in the warehouse at Fine Fare. Then I got a job that paid a lot better at 'Bourne Chemicals' so I went from earning around nineteen pounds a week to seventy pounds, doing shift work processing red lead. I told them I was eighteen years old although I was only seventeen at the time. No-one bothered checking and so I got away with it.

I had set my heart on a drum kit, a Premier D717 that was for sale for seven hundred and fifteen pounds in Counterpoint Music in Stevenage. I put a seventy pounds deposit down straight away. Then I worked nights and days, emptying 450° ovens full of red lead, with a small metal shovel on a long arm. I had to melt two different types of lead bars weighing sixty pounds, every ten minutes, every shift. We worked in pairs, wearing boiler suits and masks on all shifts, with a blood test at the end of every week. It was a dangerous job and not many people would do it, but it got me what I wanted. Then, on the morning of my last ten to six shift, I got a lift to the crossroads at Stevenage Road in Knebworth from my foreman who lived there. We said our farewells after eleven solid months of working together. Then I walked up the early morning quiet hill over to the town centre with six hundred and fifty pounds in cash plus five pounds for delivery, that I had saved. I waited for the shop to open and paid for it to be delivered the next day. It had taken a lot of hard work to get the money. While most people I knew were hanging out and going to the pub, all I did was work, occasionally treating myself to cooking a nice breakfast in between shifts for myself and Colette, my girlfriend.

Once I had paid for the drum kit, I left the job at Bourne Chemicals and answered an advert for a drummer in the *Melody Maker*. That was when I started playing in a local rock band. I got a new job at a Loctite super glue warehouse picking and sending super glue of every kind all around the world. A year later, at nineteen years old, I became an assistant telephone engineer for GC Communications for ten months, which took me all over the place – London one day, Birmingham the next, then I would be installing a multi-core cable to a telephone exchange in Dungeness Nuclear Power station down on the Kent coast. That's where I was staying, in a local B&B, in December 1980, when the landlady woke me up with the news, 'John Lennon has been shot!'

Like millions of other music fans worldwide, I was heart-broken to have lost such a talent, and in that way. We took half the day off, finishing at lunchtime, then spent the afternoon in the pub listening to *Just Like Starting Over* on the jukebox.

After I had finished this job, I managed to crash land on the streets again for a bit. Having spent some time living in various houses, part of me wanted more than I had, and I reached the stage where I wanted something permanent.

All I had ever really wanted to be was a drummer – nothing that special. Although, being a twenty-year-old inexperienced player with very little prospects, I knew I was in trouble when I found myself using my only clothes as toilet paper one night when I was making my way back to the woods in Tewin. This was where I had a camp in the woods made of plastic sheets, with nothing but the cold earth on which to shiver through the night.

At this point in my life, I had spent the last nine years on and off the streets. Sometimes it was my choice; sometimes it was just part of the unfortunate circumstances I found myself in. However, I chose carefully where I slept and woke, though sometimes I would simply become exhausted from walking miles from place to place. Added to this was a serious lack of food, then I would just fall to the ground and sleep wherever, whenever.

The members of the rock band had all left for University. I enjoyed playing in a lot of different types of bands in and around the London and home counties area. I had become a bit of a known person who would play for anyone, so my days were often full of drumming but also mostly unpaid. Then I joined a group in Stevenage called Face to Face, who played electro-pop that was also a bit funky. I filled in for their absent drummer one day in a recording session, and their bass player, Geoff Gascoyne, asked the band to take me on because we had that musical telepathy thing instantly. We played a lot doing some local low-key gigs; we recorded a lot and made some nice, interesting music. I learnt a lot of new things and the job often came with a sofa for a night or two, which made sense to me.

One afternoon while waiting to do a band practice session, I met a guy who said he worked on the American Army and Air Force bases in Germany, so I asked if there were drums out there that I could use.

'Yes,' he said. 'There are also people to play music with, and places to play, on and off the bases.'

Anyway, after a chat about me being able to stay on the American base in the barracks, I just said it sounded good to me and I would arrange to get out there with a couple of other people, who would play, too.

We exchanged contact details and a plan was put in place to get over there to play music, sometime in the near future.

*

In early 1980 I was pretty much homeless again, and I just lived hand to mouth. On one winter evening, I was doing one of my twenty odd mile walkabouts, ending up in Tewin. A few days before, some local friends of mine had said there was an American kid who had moved in up the road and I should meet him.

So I was the only person in the Rose and Crown pub, as it had just opened at six p.m. Five minutes later, this kid walked in and straight away I knew he must be the kid from America. He looked as if he had just walked off an American west coast beach. Anyway, we got talking and sure enough, it was the kid they had mentioned to me – all the way from Palo Alto in California. His name was Derek Devi Wallace, and we hit it off straight away, exchanging stories about England and America.

After a couple of drinks he said, 'Keythe, you must come and meet my family,' and that was that. I went from kipping in a bus shelter at the end of Desborough Drive to sleeping in the most beautiful, peaceful house I had ever been in. We had quite a few months of hanging out together, and it was really strange how that should have happened then... of all the times I had lived rough, and it was at that point I really needed some kind of stable shelter, away from trouble. This gave me a real ray of hope. The times I spent with Mary Ann, Don, Derek, and Harley taught me a side of life I had not really seen or ever been a part of before, a *family* side.

Even though my time with them was short-lived, what I had learnt and felt from them was and will be priceless forever. A very beautiful thing that gave me great hope and something magically special.

*

By this time, people from my less desirable background were knocking on the door for me to leave and go to Germany. So, with a small drum kit and six pounds and fifty pence in my pocket, I left for the American army base in Stuttgart to play music. Three of us left on the ferry in a Hillman Imp packed with the small drum kit, guitars and a few items of clothing.

It was 7 March 1981. Brian, who played bass, and Bob who sang and played guitar, had a lot more money secretly stashed than I had, although I knew they did not want me to know that. They seemed more prepared for the possibility of failure, and had family homes to return to if they did. Failure did not bother me. I was just going to 'wing it' and play.

We reached the Grenadine barracks in Stuttgart. It was on a fairly large site on a hill, where there was staff and office accommodation and a canteen. There were all sorts of people from all over the world working there. Some were military, some were military intelligence officers and various others, who did everything from cleaning army goods to fixing aircraft at the nearby airbase, as well as military police or just CIA personnel. I received a lot of weird looks from the intelligence community at first, but I managed to blend in after they had paid me a visit one evening. They asked me two simple questions: my full name and date of birth and then my dad's full name, date and place of birth.

'Winstead Williams, 14.7.1929, Westmoreland, Jamaica,' I said.

They muttered a few words to each other that I could not distinguish.

'Okay, that's all we need to know for now. If Rudy turns up, tell him you have spoken to us, okay?' they said before leaving the room.

Rudy was in charge of the barrack buildings. I had already met one of the agents who had asked me the two questions through a mutual friend and after that evening, I just acted as though I was meant to be there.

On our first day there, we had gone into town and done some busking. We had a good crowd and made a few Deutsche marks. It was nice to be away from the political and social unrest of England, going through all the riots and unemployment. The British government was preparing for war, rattling the sabre with Argentina over the Falkland islands, although it was still a year and one month away from being an undeclared war.

It was great playing music with the American and German people. We had a lot of fun and so long as you had an American member in the group, you could use the music studios on the bases. So I had access to nice American drum kits and Ziljian cymbals, which were very beautiful things indeed. We played a few lunchtime/evening meal background music things for high ranking military personnel. We had to play sensible, safe, middle of the road songs.

There were no punk songs allowed; it had to be easy listening type rock. Anyway, being poor in Germany was so much better than being poor in England at that time.

I had been there just a couple of weeks and was getting used to it when Dave, whose room we were all staying in, and also my contact who had a proper job in the American army, told me that a guy called Charlie wanted to meet me. He was coming over later that evening to chat to me about the Ancient Americas. This was something I had talked a lot about with Dave.

'You will like Charlie. He is a really nice guy and if you are lucky, he will bring you some cake, he usually does when he visits,' he said.

I asked Dave who Charlie was.

'Charlie? He's a high ranking member of the military who has been in service all his adult life. He knows everything there is to know about Ancient America because he has seen it all and studied it for years. Don't worry, he is a great guy,' he explained.

∗

Sure enough, Charlie turned up later with a chocolate marble cake. I made us both a pot of tea and we started chatting. He told me some amazing stories of his travels around the world to different places, all of which had ancient sites he had researched for the American military. He must have been in his late fifties or early sixties. He said that he had witnessed the horrors of wars and had first-hand knowledge of the suffering this brings to anyone who takes part in these conflicts. He had tried to go back into society in America after his war experiences, but just could not cope with it, so he re-enlisted and signed up for life.

He then wanted me to elaborate on what I had told Dave – about how I believed that American ancient history was a lot older than the history books told us it was. I explained what I had read in the library and that the Spanish diaries of the American Indians being 'savages' had to be wrong. The stonework on a lot of the sites in Central and South America was not the work of savages. Their knowledge of the stars and mathematics was second to none, in my opinion.

Their ingenious underground irrigation system, built in the deserts around the Nazca Plateau, is still going thousands of years later. Then there is the fact they somehow managed to draw perfectly straight lines across the tops of mountains from the Nazca Plateau – surely this could not be the work of simple savages, moving stones weighing many tons up mountains. The super advanced otherworldly quality of the granite stone cutting remains unexplained by archaeologists in Puma Punku. This architecture is super advanced and unique; there is nowhere else in the world that has anything quite like it on such a vast scale.

The 'savages' label was passed on and used throughout history to cover up the complete annihilation of the people there which ran alongside the plunder of what was left of an advanced civilisation's wealth. Then came the second wave of people from all over Europe and beyond. They had a much greater thirst for slaughter that was even more barbaric than the Spanish conquistadors. This often led to the stark choices some Indians had to make of either helping the European hunters, or becoming the hunted themselves. Those who did neither ended up, more often than not, in tragic circumstances on reservations, starving to death or being systematically removed to make way for 'progress'. Then, quietly and mostly undocumented by history, they were slaughtered in their thousands upon thousands. This wave took the American Indians to the verge of extinction, while not only their mineral wealth and written history was being taken by force, but also their lands that they had inhabited for millennia.

Suddenly, there was a knock on the door. The driver to take Charlie home had arrived. Before he left, Charlie wished me good luck in my search for the 'answer,' although I was not sure what he meant by that.

Sitting in the large barrack room after he had gone, I felt as though he had given me a crash course in Ancient History... as if he had given me his expert nod of approval, that I was on the right track. It felt as though he was looking down from the top of the 'Tree of Knowledge' at me negotiating the bottom branches. Through most of our conversation I had felt out of my depth; quite a few times he mentioned places I had never even heard of or read about. I just listened to what he had to say and at the same time I tried to learn something about all the major archaeological sites from the first-hand accounts of his knowledge, including, Easter Island, Puma Punku and the Nazca plateau.

It was the first time in my life that I had spoken to anyone who had such a vast amount of first-hand knowledge and experience of these places. He was not just spewing out crazy theories, he was giving me the cold, hard facts. Even though I was to never meet him again, he made a good impression on me that gave me the strength to follow my own intuition. I was beginning to doubt my thoughts before meeting him. Before speaking with Charlie I was starting to believe there was nothing else of greatness left in the world to discover, but afterwards, my quest was revitalised and renewed.

*

As far as music went, it was a great time playing with American people from places that included Texas, Illinois, Washington and California, and then with people from other countries, including Mexico, Afghanistan, Brazil and the locals from Germany.

One night, I played part of the bass line to *Walking on the Moon* on a sitar to a group of people from Afghanistan who had invited me to dinner. We could only speak in sign language, because we did not know each other's language, so they made physical gestures, pointing at me because they knew that tune. I was invited to play for them again and I was paid in lovely food.

There were a lot of trained musicians on the base, so I learnt a lot of new things because they were much more professional and trained than I was at that time. Drumming is much more of an art form in American education, especially military drumming. There is such a thing in England; it is just not as popular or accessible to the uninitiated.

I asked an American music instructor about the training and skills I was witnessing on a daily basis.

'It doesn't mean they are any better than you,' he told me. 'You may play things they can't, and vice versa – everyone plays differently.'

'Oh yeah,' I replied, 'brilliant!'

Then he went on to explain that every single successful drummer had a style of their own. Every one of them is different. That conversation was inspirational to me.

*

I spent the early eighties travelling between England and Germany, mostly on my own as Brian had gone off to Bavaria after about a month. He did show up to play bass at one festival in the Black Forest. Bob had returned to England after six months to be with his girlfriend. So I started doing a lot of busking, playing guitar; mainly blues. Bob did make one more visit. That was when he told me that my girlfriend, Colette, was seeing someone else, although when I spoke to her on the phone, she assured me that this was not true.

Around April 1983, I decided to return to England, although

it took a while because I was flat broke. I put my guitar, mini-amp and mini Casio keyboard with on board drum machine, in a train station locker. However, I did not realise the lockers only stayed locked for a certain amount of time. When I returned, the locker was empty. Everything was gone, and so was the possibility of selling the equipment and using the proceeds to buy a ticket home to England.

Eventually, after a few weeks of hanging around, the British Embassy gave me an American Express card to go to the travel agents and get a ticket back to England. When I arrived back in Dover, they held my passport at customs and issued me with a bill to pay, to get my passport back.

Once I got back, I went to see my girlfriend, who I had spoken to on the phone the day before I arrived. It was early, around seven a.m., when I knocked on her door, expecting her to answer. Her sister opened the door and said she was not there, she was staying at her friend's house. This was very odd because she knew I was going to be there that morning.

I then went to visit a Jamaican lady friend of mine, who was a good friend of my dad. She was very pleased to see me as I had kept in touch with her when I was away, and she always updated Dad whenever he rang her. She prepared me a plate of beans and rice that she had already cooked, as she could clearly see I needed a meal inside me. Then, in an indirect way, in between saying how much better my life would have been if she had been my mother, she sort of said that Colette was with someone else now. I heard her say it, but it did not register, as I had only spoken to Colette yesterday and she assured me that we were good.

However, I called round at Colette's the next morning, and she told me herself that we were done. She did not want to say that she had someone new and I did not say much or push her into revealing her new personal life to me. It was all my own fault;

I had gone off to Germany in search of success, only to return penniless, unsuccessful, and homeless.

✳

Although I was broken hearted, I did not want to show it. It was going to be a new start for me. I thought at least I would be able to get my drums, records, clothes, tape recordings, poems, and songs from Peg. After all, I had paid her up front to look after my stuff while I was away, and she had assured me that she would do just that.

As soon as I walked through the door, the look on her face spoke volumes. She looked like she had just seen a ghost.

Before I could say, 'I have come to get my stuff,' she did one of her middle of the conversation things, as though she was scoring a point against what she knew I was about to say.

'Well, I didn't think you were coming back, so I got rid of it all,' she said, sneering dismissively.

I was too tired to have a row with her about it; it was not the right time. I was already upset enough, and I did not want to land myself in a load of trouble if I kicked off about it.

With my best false smile and as much sarcasm as I could muster, I said, 'Thanks, Peg, I knew I could rely on you!' and then walked out.

When I left I went out of the back door and down the garden path, where I noticed she'd had a bonfire recently. In it were the burnt up remains of my drum stool, a hanging-tom and a mohair jumper that George had given me. I did not bother going back inside and asking her about it. I was too angry because I knew she had sold the rest of the stuff to whoever.

It was at that moment that I gained a bit more control of my temper, which is always a good thing. To confront Peg was pointless and I knew that conversation was not going to change a thing. I was more disappointed in myself for paying her and being stupid enough to believe she would keep her side of our agreement.

*

I was back in England. Back with no money, no home, no job, no drums or cymbals, no guitar, no amp, no keyboard, no clothes, no girlfriend, no records, no demo-recordings, no rehearsal or gig recordings, no songs and no poetry except the rap poetry that was going on in my head that was too X-rated to consider making a song with back then.
I walked very slowly and wearily up the hill to Tewin. I found a nice quiet spot in the woods near the chalk pits, then I sat down and became still and at one with this unforeseen sad situation. I watched the day turn to night and contemplated my options for the future, which did not take very long.

I had been in bad situations like this before, but this was not just one or two issues to sort out. This time everything needed sorting out and I had to make sure I never ended up in such dire straits again. In the last two days I had walked miles. I had not eaten or drunk anything for over thirty hours, since Sadie gave me the beans and rice meal. I had reached the lying down stage and exhaustion was setting in fast. Then I just fell to one side and it felt like slow motion; my eyes could see the blades of grass close to my eyes that were becoming blurred, then I rolled over onto my back. I looked up at the stars in flight overhead. My eyes began to slowly close, and just before I slipped into a deep sleep I took comfort in this thought, *It could be worse, it could be raining.*

Chapter Four

Lost in Space

If you ever happen to be so unlucky that you end up becoming down and out, living on the streets, remember this one thing – there is always a chance of being lucky. This is a good thought to have when you have nothing, because then having nothing becomes a chance of having something.

I opened my eyes, and it took a moment to recall yesterday's blues. Once that memory had fully sunk in, I had to start living with the reality of it all. I woke up fairly early as the April morning mist rolled over the ground like knee-high fog and the pale sunlight bounced off the morning dew. Squeezing my tongue against the roof of my mouth, trying to stimulate some moisture, whilst checking how numb I was, I then pulled my damp trousers away from sticking to my legs. I started walking to the upper green football pitch where I could use a water tap at the end of an open garden. As there was no gate, it never felt like trespassing. There was also a tap at St. Peter's church that the gardener used, half a mile away. Most days living rough started like this, along with the sound of beautiful birdsong. This was a sound that told me I had successfully made it to the next day. Then, once I was awake, the decision of where to go that day would begin.

I would have to take into consideration the distance that I would be walking, the impact on energy levels and most importantly, the food possibilities of my destination. I would often walk past houses where I knew people, in the hope of bumping into them. This may lead to receiving a few pity coins, a sandwich, or a cup of tea. I would rarely turn down any offers of support when living in such circumstances. Even a sit down in the normality of a house would help to recharge my batteries, physically and mentally.

Sometimes, I would walk ten miles or more to call on a friend. This would sometimes be awkward because I could not say things were going really well, when they clearly were not. Then I would sense that I was making them feel uncomfortable and obligated to my dilemma.

At that point, I would say, 'Nice to see you, thanks for the tea,' and leave. I felt bad for them when they had the embarrassment of having to ask me to leave or say how they would like to help but were unable to because of this or that. After all, how can anyone really help a down and out? Just by giving you a place to stay for the night and then having to ask you to leave the next day. That can be a great help but it's not a solution to the problem. I was embarrassed enough by my predicament, without making my friends feel uncomfortable by my problems as well. A cup of tea, a sandwich, a few coins, a pair of clean socks, a blanket, a box of matches or even a bath if I really got lucky… these were all good signs that you were on the road to recovery. It's always hard not to burden people with your problems, especially when they ask how you are, and you don't want to lie to them.

Avoiding that 'conversation,' while wandering from place to place, became the norm. Some days I would walk twenty or thirty miles until I got so tired, I would just drop to the ground and sleep wherever I landed.

*

One night I was visiting a drummer friend of mine and it was getting dark outside so I thought I'd best be going. Once outside I was just too tired to walk, and spotted a square area at the side of the flats, enclosed by a wooden fence. It was a tip, where people from the flats had dumped all their rubbish. Right in the centre was an old armchair with no seat, but it had a torn canvas just enough to cover the springs. How could I say no to that? As the night wears on, the cold starts to descend from above in stages. Each hour gets colder and colder until around four thirty a.m. then, although the skies are still submerged in the dark of the night, you can feel the heat of the sun hitting the earth, even though you can't see it. The nights often consisted of ten or maybe twenty minutes of repeated rounds of sleep. Each of these rounds of sleep was broken by an alpha jerk, or a rat running over me, until it was birdsong time. Shortly after this I could hear people waking up, flushing toilets, turning on their radios, and cars starting up before being driven away to work. That's when it was time to move on to someplace else. There really was no better feeling after a night of sleeping rough than when the sun started its journey through your clothes to your skin, then slowly warming your organs inside.

*

During the months that followed, I slept in hedges, woods, bus shelters, old chairs, abandoned cars, sheds, phone boxes, train stations, trains, graveyards and even in bin rooms. One night I rolled myself up in an old carpet that someone had thrown out into a bin room. It was a bitterly cold night and the carpet was warm, so I managed to get some sleep. In the morning because I was warm, I did not want to move and so I stayed put. Then a man came into the room with his black bin liners full of rubbish. I thought he would see me rolled up in the carpet, so I rolled out of it across the bin room floor and sprang to my feet. The man stared at me, open-mouthed and confused, holding a black bag in each hand and his right foot holding the bin room door open.

'Good morning! Lovely day,' I said and held the door open for him as he put his bags in a dustbin. Then he walked out of the bin room and I walked off in the opposite direction into a very sunny morning that energised me with its heat, like a breakfast for the Soul. However, being on the streets without having easy access to a bath or water was beginning to take its toll on my general health. My body was covered in sore splits of dry skin that cracked and bled when I moved and were at times very painful. At this time, I had been down and out for six months since returning to England from Germany.

*

Word reached me that my Uncle Peter had given my friend, Stephen Waters, a letter for me. This was a very rare thing because I never really got letters, being homeless. The letter was to tell me that Kit was in the QEII Hospital, very unwell and dying from cancer. There was also a letter to me from Kit, in which she wrote that I was to make something of myself that she would be proud of. Basically, she advised me to be anything other than what I was at this time. It was about a ten-mile walk across country to the hospital. However, it was a race against time, so I left immediately after I had read the letters.

*

Now, I had not been to the QEII Hospital for a very long time. As I made my way across country through Datchworth, Tewin, Panshanger then down Hanside Lane to the hospital, I recalled the day I first met and spoke to the Queen of the United Kingdom. It was on the day she opened the hospital on 22 June 1963, when I was two and a half years old. On that day, Dolly had enthusiastically told me that we were going to meet Her Majesty the Queen. It was then that I thought, *Oh great! She will take me home with her and I will live happily ever after.* I don't know why I thought this. In my young mind, I had a fairy tale image of a beautiful woman who would insist on becoming my proper Mum.

Dolly and I were at the railings with all the crowd cheering and waving flags as the Queen came towards us. I prepared myself to be lifted over the railings by her when she picked me out of the crowd. Then she was standing there in front of me, talking to Dolly.

'Oh, your Majesty, this is Keythe,' Dolly said as she introduced me.

The Queen looked over the railings at me.

'Hello,' she replied, 'are you having a nice day?'

'You're not the Queen,' I said indignantly. I looked up at Dolly. 'She is not the Queen!'

Dolly of course was embarrassed, 'Yes! This *is* the Queen, Keythe.'

The Queen paused for a second as though I might suddenly realise it was her, then change my mind and say, 'Oh yes, so it is. Sorry, Your Majesty, I didn't recognise you without your crown.'

As she still didn't lift me over the railings and take me away, I was not going to believe it really was her. Then she smiled at me, looked at Dolly who dipped into a semi-curtsey and moved on, greeting the long line of people as she advanced towards those waiting to see her officially open the hospital. I had refused to accept that she was the Queen, because she clearly had no intention of taking me home. I stayed by the railings waving my flag, waiting for the real Queen who was going to take me home and adopt me. Slowly, the cheering and excitement of the crowd dissipated into the distance. Dolly fetched me an ice cream to see if she could persuade me to go home, but I refused to move. Then I saw a blonde-haired lady speaking in an American accent across the walkway from me, taking pictures. She saw me on the other side of the railings and walked over towards me. I was still sitting down in protest mode and waved my flag, thinking maybe this is the lady who has come to take me home? One last chance to be scooped up and whisked away.

She looked the part as she moved directly towards me, clicking her big camera. Then she knelt down on the other side of the railings and took a few more photographs. The other children behind me were wondering why the naughty boy was now having his picture taken. I just assumed they would all know I was waiting for the Queen, who was going to take me home with her. Then the lady who was taking the photos of me spoke to Dolly before walking away. I thought, *well it looks like no-one is going to take me home today.*

I remember it like it was yesterday and I am sure the Queen saw the funny side of it, at least I hope she did. After all she did give me a big smile when she heard me say she was not the Queen. She probably heard a lot of kids say that sort of thing.

Around forty years later, in 2004, I was visiting my Uncle Peter Jones who lived a few hundred yards up the road from the QEII Hospital. That was when he told me the story.

'I've got something for you and a story you might not know about,' he said.

'What's that then, Peter?'

'You might not remember this, but when you were very young you met the Queen of England and according to Dolly, you made quite a fuss. You told her she was not the Queen. As I say, you were very young and did not know any better. Anyway, the next day you were on the front page of the Lemsford Times and you were famous!' He smiled. 'Apparently, Dolly had told everyone what had happened, including the lady who took the pictures of you that day.'

'Yes, Peter, I remember it as clear as anything.'

'That's good then, because I have got this for you.' He gave me a copy of the photo that appeared on the front page of the newspaper. The picture showed me sitting down behind the railings, waving my flag and staring into the camera. I was two years, seven months and eight days old.

*

Anyway, as I walked onto the driveway of the QEII Hospital that early Sunday evening, I passed the very spot where I met the Queen, although that was twenty-one years ago, and a lot had changed for me since then.

I went into the hospital and found the room where Kit was. My Uncle Peter was just leaving.

Now Kit was always a good influence on me. She never minced her words; direct and to the point was always the way she communicated.

As soon as I saw Kit sitting in an armchair next to her bed, I was shocked. Her once thick black hair had mostly fallen out and her skin was very puffy as though she was going to burst, and it was covered in red-purple patches. I felt so sad to see her like this because we both knew she did not have long to go. This moment was to be our last and if I was ever going to respectfully listen to her, I knew that this was the time I had to do it.

'Now,' she said straight away, 'Keythe, I want you to promise me you will do as I tell you, because if you don't, they will see you dead, do you understand me?'

'Yes, I understand,' I replied.

'Right. Open that drawer, take the money (it was £1.64p) and go get yourself something to eat. Then go to my house, and round the back the kitchen window is broken by the handle – I broke it. Let yourself in and sleep there in my bed, only for one night. Then tomorrow, get yourself as far away from Peg and the others as you possibly can. They will see you dead if you don't, okay?'

'Okay,' I nodded. 'Are you going to be okay?'

'Things don't look good for me, Keythe, but you make sure you do something good with yourself, okay.'

'I will,' I told her. Then she kissed me goodbye and I left.

✱

The next day, after sleeping at her house as she had told me to do, I realised just how hard getting away as far as possible was going to be, considering I was penniless and down and out with very little prospect. I left Garden City early and made my way to Stevenage Library to read. Over the past six months since returning to England, I had done my research there whenever I could. I had managed to read the complete works of Nostradamus and many other ancient books. I never took the books out, not only because I did not have a permanent address but also for fear of losing them. So I hid them in the library where no-one else would find them until I had finished reading them.

The fact that the complete works of Nostradamus had been written in French and translated into English was a challenge for me, but what he wrote about in the book itself was very interesting.

A couple of days later, I went to see Peg. I am not sure why I did this after I had promised Kit I would get as far away from her and the others as I possibly could. However, to keep the promise I had made was going to take a good plan and a lot of luck, both of which were in short supply at this time.

I had been there for about ten minutes when the phone rang. Peg answered and said it was for me. It was Peg's sister, Wendy.

'Hello, Keythe. Kit has died,' she said in a very cold, matter of fact way.

'Okay,' I replied sadly, and put the phone down. 'I'm off then Peg, see you later. Bye!' I shouted to Peg in the other room as I left.

I was upset but I knew it was coming and that was the day it did, 6 November 1984. Dolly had died around the same time on 10 November, a few days before my tenth birthday. Kit's death was a few days before my twenty-fourth birthday.

It was very bitterly cold that November. I was sleeping in the open plan bus shelter at the top of Desborough Drive in Burnham Green. Half brick and half wood with a lovely wooden bench that makes all the difference to heat retention on those very long, cold nights. The weather was the kind you get when heavy snowfall is imminent… grey and strangely warm, then later when the night came, so did the snow. I sat in the bus shelter watching it get deeper and deeper until it was a foot or more deep. It was lovely and quiet, which meant no traffic, four wheel drives were not two a penny in those days. As I laid my head down on the bench to try and get some sleep, the heavy snow was falling in what looked like slow motion. The sense of peace and tranquillity was a very beautiful thing. I drifted in and out of sleep, occasionally opening my eyes to make sure the snow was still there. The morning came round pretty quickly so I helped myself to a couple of handfuls of snow, to wash the night from my mouth in the crisp, bright blue morning of this sunny day.

The snow was deeper than it was last night and there were still no signs of life. I began to contemplate my next move, when a man came walking up to the bus shelter from a house in Desborough Drive and sat down next to me. I was a little nervous that he was going to ask me to move on, but he didn't. After all, I couldn't say I was waiting for a bus, as the snow was way too deep for that excuse. Instead and to my surprise, he struck up a friendly conversation. He began by asking me why I had been sleeping in the bus shelter. I explained my situation of how I needed to get my act together, to find a job and somewhere to live. The chat was pleasant enough, and he did sort of advise me that staying there any longer than I needed could be very hazardous to my health in these weather conditions. Our brief conversation got me thinking of possible solutions to my problems. When he said goodbye and walked back down Desborough Drive to his house, I gave twenty minutes' thought to what I could do or who could I call.

All I had in the world at that point in my life was in an old, torn, yellow rucksack. It contained a photo album, a book of poems that I had written that year, a pack of AE Waite tarot cards that were a present from Stephen Waters, and some very rare pictures of Jimi Hendrix I had bought from a girl called Lyn.

The previous day, I had walked ten miles or more in the freezing cold and my feet were now completely frozen numb. When you get snow cold, walking makes your feet really sore. The bones in your feet feel as though they are going to push through your skin when you walk, creating a very painful burning sensation with every step you take. There was a poster of a disabled person in a wheelchair pinned up in the bus shelter, which was unusual. I think it was a Remembrance Day poppy poster, or a charity poster. I had been looking at the poster before the man came and spoke with me and I thought how hard it must be to be a wheelchair user. If I found myself in that situation right now, there would absolutely no chance of me wheeling myself through this snow.

Anyway, I started looking through my photos and came across a picture given to me by a guitarist friend of mine called M Jackson earlier in the year. I had met him through answering an ad for a drummer in the Melody Maker seven years previously. I looked on the back of the photo and it said:

> *'Remember, Remember Crystal Palace,*
> *A place where you may fear no malice.*
> *The room at the top where you can stay,*
> *Until your troubles go away.'*
>   *M J 21.5.1984*

I reached my frozen hand into my pocket and rummaged around carefully, trying to pull out the few coins that I had… just enough to make a phone call. I decided to ring him from the phone box three hundred yards or so up the road. I put the photos away and stood up slowly, then I tested the level of soreness in my feet that needed to be overcome to walk. I carefully reached the edge of the bus shelter that was not affected by the snowfall, before putting my first foot forward into the deep snow. As my foot sank into the virgin snow on the first step towards the telephone box, the numbness of my frozen feet came to a slow crescendo of burning pressure pain. It felt as though the bones of my feet were going to tear though my skin, as they painfully met the snow compacting beneath my shoes. The pain increased with every step and the numbness impaired my balance. Each step was more painful than the last. I was almost certain my bones had broken through my skin, as I could feel the wetness in my shoes. I stopped and looked down, although I did not want to. There was no trace of blood and the wetness that I felt was caused by the sun melting the ice on my shoes. Lack of food was beginning to blur my vision, along with the sunlight reflecting on the snow making it seem like I was walking on frozen white light. Everything was tinged with all the colours of the rainbow. Then I took a few more steps and I was almost there. If anyone had seen me walking, they may well have mistaken me for a very old person who had forgotten his walking stick, out for a very slow walk, on this beautifully cloudless, winter's morning.

Finally, I reached the phone box. The last few steps were the hardest, for fear of falling over and not being able to get up again. I reached out my left hand, trying to bend my sore, frozen fingers, and readied myself to pull open the snow-jammed phone box door. It took all the little strength I had left, to pull it open and get inside.

I reached into my pocket, although I could not feel my fingers or the coins I knew I had counted in the bus shelter. Once I had the money in my hand, I dialled the number. With each ring I could hear my inner voice saying, 'Please pick up the phone,' over and over.

'Hello,' said a voice at the other end. It was Matthew.

'Hey, Matthew,' I said, 'it's Keythe here. How are you doing?'

'I'm okay, thanks,' he replied. 'How are you?' he replied.

'I'm homeless, at the moment, but I'm okay.'

'Listen, if you can get yourself down here to Peckham, I've got a chair that opens out into a bed that you can use until you get yourself sorted out. It's not much but you're welcome to it if you want it?' he so very kindly said.

'Okay. For sure that would be great because I am really stuck right now,' I said with much appreciation.

He gave me his new address 24, Tyrrell Road, Peckham. I said I would be there in a couple of days and I would phone him when I got there. I put the phone down, extremely relieved. I was getting away from a bad situation and off the streets. I was also keeping the promise I had made to Kit to get away from Peg and the others who wished me wrong.

I then walked miles from here to there and back again, trying to raise the train fare by begging a few pence from whoever I thought might help. After a few more days begging on the streets, I had managed to get together enough money to get the train, bus, and a little bit of food at the end of the journey.

∗

I arrived at Matthew's first thing on a Sunday morning. It was quite a nice area, with old four-storey buildings. I was pretty early, so I found a shop and bought some food with the money I had left from the train and bus fare. I sat outside the shop and although it was a cold morning in late November 1984, the sun was shining bright. It gave me the kind of heat that replenishes you when you live on the streets.

I couldn't wait to finally get a rest. I was physically exhausted from the cold weather and lack of food. It felt as if my body was hanging on a very cold skeleton; my muscles burnt every-time I moved. I went to a phone box to call Matthew.

'Great, you made it,' he said. 'Come and meet my house mates; we are having some breakfast.'

I walked over the threshold of the house, said hello to everyone and ate some welcome porridge. Matthew then showed me the sofa chair. I opened it out and he gave me a blanket. I thanked him very much and even though it was around eleven a.m., I went to sleep straight away. I stayed in bed for eight days and nights. The inner coldness was extremely hard to expel from my bones, as was getting my body to feel a normal temperature again.

All in all, it took me three months to feel normal again, and rid myself of the physical damage I had sustained from living rough on the streets in the bitter winter cold.

Matthew knew my background and he had met Peg a few times. We had become friends through music. He had always been amazed at the fact that he, his brother, Neil, and their friend,

Martin Lomax, had walked into Counterpoint Music in Stevenage where they saw the Premier D717 drum kit.

'Wouldn't it be great if we had a drummer with that kit,' they had said to each other.

Then the first time we played together, when I auditioned for their group, after answering their *Melody Maker* advert, I had that very same drum kit.

Matthew's mother, Kathy, was a nurse and she knew Peg because she had treated her during some home visits, when Peg was recovering from cancer. His father was a Psychology Professor, who I would often chat to about political psychology and the things I could see coming in the future. These things I could see coming were like stages being set by political parties who practised the dark Orwellian '1984' arts of 'Big Brother,' manipulating the media to direct opinion and control of the minds of the masses. These ideas that I had were formed from what I saw, heard, and read. I would analyse these things, seeing the aims and outcomes before they became reality. In a lot of ways, all I was really doing was analysing words, tones and the rhythmic timings used in their delivery to reach a fast conclusion as to the meaning and direction of the unspoken. These conclusions I found were contained within the speakers' minds and could often be heard between the lines as they spoke. Very simple really, although it can make you a target for criticism if you express your thoughts to the wrong person. You run the risk of being labelled 'nuts'. Like predicting that cash would be made illegal for some reason and money in the future becomes digital only. Then one day the whole digital world crashes and what you had is no longer. Now who would have the power to do that and to what end? Chaos used to usher in a one-party world, a controlled 'digital world poverty prison' for the masses. One currency, one bank, one rule… one day?

*

Anyway, Kathy always said that she thought I should be proud that I never let coming from the poor side of town stop me crossing over to the other side of the tracks, to mix and be friends with her sons in the more affluent side of town. There has always been a division between middle and lower classes, snobs in both classes, although, unlike a lot of other people, I didn't let that stop me… something she said she had rarely seen, although my motive was not the affluence they possessed. It was simply my secret thirst for the knowledge they had of anything and everything.

So, once I had recovered, the upside was that Martin, a house mate of Matthew's, had a Tascam Four track tape machine that I could use. I turned some of my poems into songs using Matthew's guitars, a drum machine, a front-line echo pedal and Martin's bass guitar. When the people in the house went out to work or school, I would do some housework – cleaning and hoovering. Then I would record songs to play to people when they came home. I did very reluctantly take a job at McDonalds in Peckham High Street because it was rightly decided that it would *be a means to an end* by a student house meeting without me. I didn't quite make it through the second week, though, and ended up getting changed out of the horrid brown plastic uniform one day before walking out halfway through a shift. This was straight after I had slipped over on a spilt milkshake and hurt my hip bone badly. Then the quick-thinking supervisor blamed me in case I made an injury claim, which I had absolutely no intention of doing. This job really was not for me; I did not see the attraction, even if you did get four pounds worth of food every shift. I know that having a job was a good thing and there are a lot worse than that one, but at that time I had other, better ideas for my life.

So I started playing drums in a rockabilly/rock 'n' roll band with Matthew and his mate, Paul, who was a big Elvis fan. We sort of changed the style of music a bit because I couldn't really play rockabilly well. They wanted to aim for more of a pop music sound, which was something I could play.

Anyway, Paul and Matthew very kindly brought me a lovely deep, marching snare drum, then I sort of started again from there. I had an old bass drum from my first kit and the cymbals. At this time, I also started playing in a few other groups around the Hertfordshire area. This drum kit was a small set up that I could easily carry on the train. Bag for the snare, bag for the cymbals, stands with bass pedal in another bag, and I could carry the small bass drum, so travelling was easy and I was doing what I enjoyed most of all.

*

In March 1985, I got a call from Stephen Waters to say he had got us a gig in the Malvern Fringe Festival in May. It sounded very grand. When I asked one of the guys in Peckham if he knew where Malvern was, he said he knew exactly where it was because he had grown up in Worcester, which is eight miles north of there. I asked him what it was like.

'It's Lord of the Rings country, a very beautiful part of England. You will love it. It has a long history of music and the arts. Famous for its spring water that runs out of springs for free at the sides of roads and has the royal seal of approval,' he said, very favourably.

Free spring water sounded good to me. I wished I had been told about this place when I was younger because I would have checked it out. I did a few weeks up and down to Stevenage, rehearsing songs that Stephen had written. The day arrived to do the Fringe Festival gig, and Stephen's mate, Peter, took me, Stephen, Shirley (Stephen's girlfriend) and her friend, Sue, in his van. We didn't have much to take, just a small drum kit, one Roland keyboard and small amp. The bass player, Paul Holland, lived in Malvern, so he was going to meet us there.

While Stephen and Peter sat in the front with the young ladies behind them, I sat in the back, playing quietly on my snare drum to the tunes on the radio. After a long four-hour drive, we arrived in sunny Malvern, where the skies were turquoise blue. As the hills came into view, I saw for myself that Kenneth was right when he said it was a very beautiful place.

We arrived at a large Malvern stone house, a few hundred yards from where Edward Elgar was buried. I could easily understand where his musical beauty came from when I saw the panoramic views and the majesty of the hills.

We checked in with the lady who had booked us to play. Although this sounds very grand, we were actually only getting door money. She rang Paul, the bass player, who said he would meet up with us in West Malvern, at The Lamb public house. She took her car and we followed in the van to the venue, driving from south east of the hills round to the west, via the north of the hills. When we started going up North Hill, the views became better and better the higher we climbed.

I could see that Peter was not paying enough attention to the road.

'Peter! Keep your eyes on the road,' I said cautiously.

'I know how to drive!' he said dismissively, and clearly not noticing a three-foot high granite wall a hundred yards ahead, on the passenger side.

'Peter! Watch the road, man,' I repeated.

BANG! He hit the wall and smashed the front passenger side of the van, puncturing the tyre and denting the side of the van. Luckily, there was a small clearing in front of an electricity sub-station right on the corner as you turned to go up to West Malvern, so he pulled in and parked. There were no injuries apart from Peter's ego in the light of his 'I know how to drive' quote just seconds before he clipped the wall. We got out to assess the damage. The van was still driveable. Then, before we managed to get the spare tyre out of the van and I could say, 'Hey Martin what are you doing here?' Stephen, Peter, Shirley, and Sue had jumped into his Ford Princess car, driving away with the parting words, 'Stay with the van we will be back in a minute.'

Martin was from Stevenage and worked as a roadie for some quite big bands. He could often be found in Stevenage selling very expensive microphones he had stolen from a warehouse in London, where bands like Pink Floyd stored their equipment. Being a roadie means you put the equipment away after the gig, although Martin had some expensive drug habits that needed his employers 'unknown' support. So, although I knew him, I didn't have much to do with him, because luckily, I never fell into the trap of doing the hard drugs thing, unlike a lot of people I knew, who saw it as a rite of passage.

Dad was always super clear on this matter.

'Keat, you no take drug that no come from ground. Them chemical, you no do. See?'

'Yes, Dad, I see.' When I said that to him, I meant that I respected his advice and his request that I avoid them.

He knew his medicines and did not subscribe to anything he could not grow, for himself or his children to consume. After all, he was a farmer for over twenty years back in Jamaica. He made me laugh because the way he put it was like an advert. It would make a great advert for today's chemical consumers. However, each to their own and all that.

*

Anyway, enough of all that; back to the crashed van on the corner by the electric sub-station as you go up the West Malvern Road. About forty minutes later, Martin turned up with an empty car and we loaded the musical equipment in it, then drove to the Lamb. I started getting the instruments inside. As soon as I saw the others, I could tell straight away what Peter and Stephen had been doing for the last forty minutes or so with their eyes pinned and vacant looks on their faces. They were both smacked out on heroin. Paul, the bass player, turned up, saw them, and wanted some.

We rushed through a very feeble, half-hearted sound check and Stephen was struggling big time. We had a break before playing, so I went to the bar. The pub was empty apart from us. I did my usual before playing; asked for some ice water to drink if I got hot. Then I turned around to find Paul, Martin, Stephen, and Peter had gone outside to consume more heroin. Shirley and Sue were sitting at a table, pretending they were unaware of what was going on outside. After thirty minutes, I asked them both to go outside and get them in to play. It wasn't really worth it, because they were all completely off their heads. Sue and Shirley managed to charm two blokes into hearing us, getting them to pay the two pounds each door money. We played two songs, then on the third both Paul and Stephen stopped halfway through, because they were too out of it. They all went outside again, and Sue and Shirley followed, so I was left with two guys who had paid for music. *How am I going to entertain these two and the barman on just the drums?* I wondered. I picked up Paul's bass guitar and checked the tuning and walked up to the microphone.

'This is a new one... it's called 'Piccadilly' (You show me yours and I'll show you mine).' Then I began a twenty-five minute improvisational reggae song with two notes, E and B. The people at the bar actually clapped when I had finished, and so did the barman, though I wasn't sure if they were clapping with relief because I had stopped. During the song, Sue and Shirley popped in trying to get me to stop, as if I should be outside having a lovely time. But I continued and did a second song – same notes, different words.

'Er, this is another new one hot off the press. It's called, 'London Town' and that includes Piccadilly.' Then away I went on my second improvised song of the night. There were no shouts for an encore, in fact the song ended because the two paying customers went next door to the other bar. When the gig was over I told myself I was not playing with this pair again. The few gigs we did do had started okay with us supporting Lee Scratch Perry. It all ended at the Lamb in Malvern with me playing solo.

∗

The next day, I persuaded the lady who organised it to give me a lift to the Marquee Club in London. A drummer friend of mine, Clifford, was playing there, but when we got there they were all just packing up. Clifford was on the stage and asked me to join him. I jumped up on the stage and then he took me into the dressing room at the back.

'Jimi Hendrix has been in this room,' he said.

Wow! I knew what he was saying, and I thought about that, so it wasn't a complete waste of time. We stayed at a house in Clapham that night, then the next day when I got back to Archway, I gave some petrol money to the lady who had given me the lift, and said I would visit Malvern again sometime soon. Two months later I did visit. It was the weekend of *Live Aid* and I watched it on television. I remember thinking I hadn't any money to give as I was completely flat broke. My total monetary and material wealth that day was less than I care to remember.

It made me realise how little I actually had, though I had only been off the streets for eight months at that point. I had taken a look around Malvern and liked it very much; it was such a beautiful part of the world and had an olde worlde peacefulness about it, reminding me a bit of Tewin.

I felt I had found the sort of place where I could be musically creative. This had moved up the charts of my top ten 'must haves' in life. So, I spent the next eighteen months before moving there either working at The Royal Northern Hospital, playing in the rock 'n' roll band, writing, or working at The Malvern Arts Workshop. When I was there, I would wait tables in the café, wash up, make drinks, be a cashier, prepare food and to end the day, scrub floors on my hands and knees after I had hoovered the café area – all for eight pounds a day. It was open from eight a.m. to six p.m. seven days a week. The whole thing took off after a lot of hard work from a lot of different people some years later.

The building was owned by the family of the main lady who ran it, and she had the vision for it all. She was also the main cook there, and dealt with a lot of the Mental Health referrals. I was her second-in-command, as her father put it whenever he introduced me to his friends, although no-one else really saw it like that as most people viewed me as some kind of minion. With the success of the place came those who wanted a taste without having to earn it, which was something I found hard to accept, especially when I was scrubbing the floors on my hands and knees after they had all gone home.

So the whole Lamb gig/Malvern Fringe Festival helped me come to the conclusion that I needed to find a way to do music with reliable people who wanted the same as I did. Changes needed to be made and the only way to make that a reality was to do it myself. Then I could write, play, and record with or without others, or what was the point in working so hard for so little in return? I had developed an addiction over the years and musical creativeness was the only cure.

*

Back in London, the rock 'n' roll band went through a few bass players, then Matthew's brother, Neil, joined which was good because we had played in a rock group together in our teenage years and he could do the job. Matthew always told the story of how Neil could sit an exam and pass with flying colours without really studying. He had a natural gift of being a bright-minded person, unlike most of us. Not long after Neil joined the group, he and Matthew moved into the large flat above the launderette in Archway Road. Paul, the singer in the band, half-owned it with his family, along with a string of launderettes across North London. I sort of moved in with them, staying there on and off unofficially. Paul would service the washing machines downstairs, collect the coins from them and put them into the boot of his Sunbeam sports car. Quite often, the suspension would be challenged by the sheer weight of the bags of coins he had collected from the four different launderettes.

Paul and Matthew did a lot of clubbing in the West End in 1985-87. It was the done thing in those days. You just were not cool if you didn't go on a regular basis. I didn't bother with it, except for once when I did a few clubs with them. That night, I ended up in 'Gossips' playing a snare drum, backing up some American guy on a piano, then Gary Mayall (John Mayall's son) on piano and his mate on violin, doing

Shake, Rattle and Roll and a few other rock 'n' roll classics. It really was great fun.

Now there was no money exchanging hands for these jams,

gigs or whatever, so I joined an employment agency to earn some money. The Aquarius Employment Agency was at the top of the Holloway Road, which was just down the road, so I went in and signed up for agency work. The next day, I got a call to go and work in a warehouse not far from Holloway prison. When I got there, it was a large room, full of boxes and boxes of music cassettes. I was like a kid locked in a sweetshop for that whole week. Then I got a call to go to The Royal Northern Hospital in Holloway Road, to be a porter. This involved my sitting reading books and occasionally taking some person down to theatre for surgery. I would do my reassuring chats as we went down in the lift, which often helped them become calm and relaxed before their procedures. I am not sure why, but I found this a very natural thing to do; I had no training whatsoever but what I did and said seemed to work for the patients. I did this for a few months for sixty-eight pounds per forty-hour week. Then I was sent to sort out the medical records files in the same hospital for ten pounds per week more. I was going to be working in an all-female office, which was different to what I had been used to in the past.

My boss was a lovely Irish lady called Mary Gallagher. All the staff, except for me, took the phone calls and sorted out medical appointments. I was left to get on with sorting the file situation out with a helper who worked a couple of days a week. This help was from another Irish lady called Mira, who would often turn up with a hangover. Then she would ask me if I would like to join her and her husband on a night out in the local pubs. I had to decline the offer on several occasions, as I was no good at drinking more than a pint; I am a lightweight drinker most of the time.

One day, I was up a ladder putting files on the top shelf. I looked down at Mira slumped against the filing cabinet, the worse for wear and noticed she did not have any eyebrows! When I delicately enquired why this was, she muttered something and then ran out of the office to the toilet, returning with eyebrows drawn on. I knew she had looked different to me for ages, but I couldn't quite figure out what it was about her. We did have a laugh when she came back, with her telling me how much she had consumed the night before. This was her regular weekend account on a Monday morning before we went to get our cheese rolls and tea from the reception area downstairs.

Where I worked, there were thousands and thousands of paper records in folders, on about twenty large racks in the back part of the large office. However, they were in no order whatsoever, so this made finding notes for doctors' surgeries very difficult and time consuming. My job was to read the orders from the ladies who had compiled lists of names from phone appointments in the main part of the office, and then I would pick the correct records for the doctors and send them to the right room.

At the end of the day I would wait for them to return and file them so that they could be easily found next time.

In my spare time, I would sort out and put into order thousands upon thousands of records by the serial numbers. They would then hopefully be in a usable order. Easy? It took me about a year, five days a week, with no holidays. Agencies don't pay holiday pay. It was a nice job really, then in the spare time I had when I was not working at the hospital I would write and play music.

Now the big thing in the mid 1980's was getting a record deal, but it had to be with a large advance, or it was not seen as worth it. Some groups managed to get good deals, but all deals came with their own terms and conditions.

The advance had to be a non-returnable advance or if it wasn't and you were not a success, you could end up paying it off doing gigs all over the place until it was paid in full. This could leave you artistically trapped, with debts to pay off. It was not an 'all wealth beyond your wildest dreams' type of thing. Anyway, we managed to get a few record companies to listen to our noise. We didn't get any interest until an A&R man from Magnet Records showed a lot of interest and turned up to hear us play our songs. He then asked for us (myself & Paul, whose group it was) to have a meeting with them at the record company office to sort out a deal. We went along and sat in this A&R man's office. He played a song from our demo tape that he wanted to release as a single, called *Sad Situation*. It was a great song that Matthew had written, and the A&R man could not get enough of Matthew's guitar solo, playing it five or six times. Then down to business, he said he wanted to press that song, release it and see if it took off. No money involved, just a record release of the song on the Magnet Record label. To me it was an easy decision with no risk of debt from an advance, just cut the record and see if it takes off. Yes please! was my answer, although I didn't say it out loud. I looked at Paul, thinking he would be asking for the contract for us to read and get back to them. I could tell by the look on his face that he was not happy about something, and then the penny dropped. Paul did not like the idea of releasing that particular song, because it was not one that he had written. We left after a while with Paul saying that he would be in touch. He considered himself the leader of the group and the main songwriter, although that should not have swayed his decision the way it did.

On the drive home, he said, 'Do you know what, I don't think it's a good deal. We can't take it if we don't get any money. We should wait for something better, with a big advance.' He made his decision clear.

When Matthew and Neil asked Paul how the meeting went, he didn't tell them the truth, although I was not there at the time when they spoke about it. I trustingly assumed he told them the full story and they had agreed with his decision that it wasn't a good deal, so we should wait for the elusive 'big deal'. I found out many years later from Matthew, that Paul just said he was waiting to hear from Magnet but never did. Now Paul, Matthew and Neil all came from well-off, middle class backgrounds; not filthy rich but wealthy enough, with loving, supportive families should they need a helping hand or a room to fall back on. If they never made any success with music, they had the cushion of family waiting in each of their futures.

I had seventy-eight pounds per week and a desire to succeed with no cushion. I had to face the harsh facts that the music business was never easy, unless you had a lot of luck and a lot of talent. Both were in short supply with me at that time, but I optimistically carried on through 1986.

*

I met a young lady called Debbie from New York, in London, and became a close friend of hers. She told me about all the people she knew in New York and that she worked in the music business. Then she told me the usual tales of the parties there with all the famous people. She seemed to know everyone and she was successful, but it was no big deal to her. Then one day, I was at Archway when the phone rang and there was a man on the other end of the phone who was softly spoken with an effeminate American voice.

'Hi, I am ringing to speak with Keythe,' he said.

'Yes hi, how can I help you?'

'I hear you're looking for a Kook,' he said.

I thought he had said cook. 'I think you may have the wrong number. We are not looking for a cook,' I said, slightly confused.

'No, no... I have the right number. You are Keythe, the person I was told to speak to,' he replied.

'I'm not sure who gave you this number, but I'm pretty sure no one here is looking for a cook. You could ring back later if you like.'

'So, you don't want a kook?'

As he said it again, I realised that he was definitely saying Kook and not cook.

'As I say, it might be better to ring back later,' I repeated.

'Ah! Okay then, bye for now.'

It was the strangest phone call. When I put the phone down, I was wondering why he said the word, 'kook' and not cook.

I mentioned the call to Matthew and Neil but neither of them had any idea who it was, then just dismissed it as a wrong number, even when I said that the man knew my name. I was confused and thought it was someone having a laugh.

Later that week, we were having a house party on the Friday night and the band was going to do a set. We were due to play when the house filled up a bit. While we were all waiting around, I sat in the bedroom next to the front room where we were due to play, with my back against the door and feet up against the wardrobe, sort of wedged in. I was in there talking to a girl I knew and her friend about the music scene. Suddenly I heard a lot of commotion outside on the landing.

'Where's Keythe?' I heard someone say.

Another voice said, 'In there.'

Hearing this, I pushed my back against the door to make it seemed locked. Then someone tried to open the door. I wasn't ready for that to happen. They must have realised I was in there as the door slightly opened and I pushed it shut again with my back, pressing my feet against the wardrobe. Then all hell broke loose. Whoever was on the other side started banging on the door.

'Keythe! Keythe!' they were not just shouting, but screaming. This went on and on, lasting ten or so minutes. There must have been three or four people, at least. After a while, it stopped. I gave it a few minutes and then I opened the door. There were these four people huddled round someone on the stairs. I could not quite believe my eyes – the man surrounded by the four people was Andy Warhol.

Then I realised he was the person going on about me needing a 'Kook,' on the phone. The only person who he would have known that I knew and had the land line telephone number, was my dear friend Debbie from New York. I looked at him and his friends, and thought, *pen, paper…*

'Hello, Mr. Warhol. Any chance you could draw me a little picture and sign it, then could I have my photo taken with you, me and the drawing in it?'

'Come on Keythe,' someone said, 'it's time to play.'

So, I went next door to a front room packed full of people in party mode, drinking and shouting. I completely forgot the first song while I was wondering why we were not all out on the stairs chatting with Mr. Warhol. I don't think many people realised he was there. Second song, I got it together and the crowd liked it. They were all having a nice time dancing away.

Andy and his friends did not stay until the end, but they taught me a very valuable lesson, after which I didn't really want my fifteen minutes of fame. That's how I knew I would not really like it… with people screaming and banging the door down? No thanks.

*

Shortly after the party, Paul suggested we have a few backing singers join the band. The next thing I knew, we had four backing singers at rehearsals – Cathy, Wendy, Lisa and Stacy, who was going out with the pop star Paul Young at the time, then later they married. It made all the difference having the backing singers, because we sounded better, and they were so much fun to have around. They didn't take the whole thing that seriously and we had a lot of laughs. It was weird seeing Stacy on the television doing an advert for Double Decker chocolate one minute, then walking through the door the next minute with a bottle of fizzy wine, getting ready to practice. She was such a beautiful person and we had a lot of laughs. Towards the end of 1986 they all left to have kids and do other things. It was not the same after they had gone. That spark of joy and fun had been replaced by the 'who wrote the song? Because if it becomes a hit, they get most of the royalties' syndrome. When you don't even have a record deal, it's all a bit silly. The best thing for me to do in this situation was to change what I was doing or ask for a fair rate of pay as a session musician. It was sad, because a band that can't share the writing process in some form, is not a band. It's a solo artist who hasn't told you that you are his back-up band. Anyway, the rock 'n' roll group did get a few gigs here and there, mainly around North London. One pub gig we did stands out in my mind more than the others; it was not far from the West End. There were a few people in the pub, and I noticed an elderly gentleman watching our set with a very keen eye. When we had a half-time break, I sat with him to drink my ice water.

'You have got 'it' my son, but your mates haven't got as much drive… the hunger, you know? Don't know what they are after, so I'm not sure about them. I watched the whole act very carefully,' he said.

I was not sure what he meant by this, but the guys were at the bar looking at me talking with this bloke. They were all happy with themselves because there were no mistakes in the songs; all the evenings of practice had paid off. The guys were calling me over to rejoin the band and I was still talking to the old fellow about all the bands he had seen back in the day.

'Lovely to meet you, mate, thanks for the tip.' I shook his hand and got back on the drums, to play the second set. His tip was, 'Find yourself a better band because these boys are not hungry enough.'

When I was packing up my two drums and two cymbals at the end of the gig, he came over to me.

'Thanks for that, and remember what I said, okay?' he said as he made his way outside.

'Yes mate, I will do. Thanks for the advice and thanks for listening, take care.'

'What advice?' Paul, the singer, asked, and I had to think on my feet.

'Oh, advice about what drums are best to use,' I replied.

I was not sure what he meant about being hungry enough because we all wanted to succeed in having a career in playing music. I certainly wanted a better situation and I am sure the rest of the group did as well.

When I got back to Archway that night, I thought about what this gent had said, and weighed it all up. Paul, the singer, had his own house and plenty of money from his launderettes, with a fairly well-off family who supported him financially through the family business. Matthew had a decent job as a graphic designer in the city, and a family who would help him if he ever needed it. Unfortunately for Matthew, even though he was the most talented one of us, he suffered from being a bit musically trapped by Paul, whom he fully accepted as being the band leader. Paul had the wannabe rock 'n' roll star ego thing, crossed with the control freak character going on. Matthew spent a long time in the cloudy mists of being a side man, where his friendship and musical loyalty were being taken for granted by Paul. Matthew was always good enough to do something much better musically without Paul. Most of us have worked for someone else's dream at some point in our lives, until the mist clears, and he thankfully split from Paul years later to do his own thing. Last time I heard from him, he was getting ready to play Glastonbury and I was very pleased for him. Neil was well on his way to being a GP. He now has his own practice and continues to be a successful GP. Beneath the rock 'n' roll character Paul had created was a real singing talent, although his inability to share and change musically stifled his own success. His talent to sound like Elvis was outstanding at times, but he wasn't really poor enough to really understand exactly where the true emotional soulfulness of Elvis was coming from. However, he and Matthew did do gigs with Scotty Moore in Europe, which validated things for them both to a point.

I needed to make a change for the better and I knew that the geezer in the pub was absolutely right; I needed to find something better. I was wasting my time being an unpaid side man trying to make Paul's dreams come true.

If nothing was happening at the weekends in my eighteen months change of plan time, I would go to Malvern, and work in the Arts Workshop. Occasionally, I would go to Stevenage to see Stephen. By this time he was working as a 'Strip-o-gram' more than playing the piano. When I did visit him, I would often find myself holding his raincoat in a market, or at a party somewhere. He would be dressed as a Zulu or a policeman, reading a poem and then kissing a young, embarrassed or very enthusiastic woman, which was often accompanied by a lot of screaming and laughing. Stephen was very good at this job and he seemed to enjoy it as his main way of earning a living.

This was a far cry from being in the group *Face to Face* with Stephen, Ricky, Steve and Geoffrey. We made some nice music together although it didn't last long as I had gone off to Germany.

Steve, the guitarist, sadly passed away in a car accident while on holiday abroad. Ricky, the singer, went to work for his Dad in the motor trade. Geoff went off to Farnham Art College; he did later find success playing bass with Jamie Cullum. I popped in to see Geoff years later when he was playing at Panshanger golf course with Jamie. We exchanged our latest music CD's. It was just before the Bridget Jones *What a Difference a Day Makes* song was a hit. He was the best bass player I have ever worked with; really good.

Stephen had some nasty habits with certain substances, and he would certainly not deny it, but that was up to him. As his friend, I worried that he would go too far and waste himself. Ironically, he introduced me to healthy food and he was a great cook of vegetarian food. He gave me shelter from the storm many times, and I owe him a lot for that, as I do with Matthew and many others who helped in my hard times.

He also introduced me to some great books about astrology, ancient beliefs, the occult, numerology and tarot cards. At the time, I thought it was all a bit hocus pocus but if you read enough, it does start to make you wonder about certain things. My interest was purely research, though. I was not a fanatic like some people who claim to fully understand it all and then become obsessive about it. 'Okay, I'm an expert in magic now,' is not something I would say after reading a book about it. However, some people do that. Fortunately for me, I did not.

My mind was changed because the books explained that these things can be used for good or bad. I had never really thought of it like that before. Stephen was a good influence on me. After reading all the books, I understood how to consider things that were different with an open mind, rather than just be judgemental and unfairly dismissive of anything new.

Stephen always had my best interests at heart. He knew an old friend of mine called Nicholas Sheffield, which for me was a good sign. Stephen encouraged me to learn to play the piano, so I have always tried to teach myself and I had theory lessons years later from Robert Norris who is a master musician. I am still learning to this day as I love the instrument so much. Stephen also insisted on buying me a set of tarot cards, because I had told him of things in the future that then came true. Most of what I had predicted to him about the future had come to me in dreams and visions. I have always had them since I was very small, and there are quite a few people who will vouch for me, with all that.

I later read that the history of tarot cards could be traced back thousands of years to ancient times in Egypt. Then forward in time when they were banned in Britain before they were brought back, disguised as playing cards. So if you bought two packs of cards you could make a seventy-eight card pack of tarot hiding in plain sight until the ban was lifted.

Stephen also showed me a lot of books that I could not understand like an A. Crowley's book on magic, and a book on bio-rhythms which looks at the patterns of the ups and downs of human physiology. However, the book that I found the most interesting was the *I-Ching Book Of Changes*. Very deep and very old. It was in this book that I first read the ancient quote, *The history of humanity is written on the face of the earth.* Nothing ever jumped off the page and engraved itself in my mind so deeply as that quote, although I did not have any real idea why that was so. I would wake up with it in my mind, I would go to sleep and it would be the last thought in my head. It was as though, somewhere very deep in my memory, I had sent myself a reminder not to forget that quote and to find out exactly what it really meant. At first, I thought it meant the historical footprint of humanity could be seen on the face of the earth, like the great wall of China, then all the buildings and monuments. However, if that was true, it still did not explain why I had the quote recurring in my mind almost constantly. If buildings were the answer and it was that simple, then why did my mind constantly keep going over it?

*

The last time I saw Stephen was not long after Phil Lynott had passed away. I was at Stephen's flat when I got a phone call to be told the very sad news.

I had first seen Thin Lizzy in 1974, when I was thirteen years old at St. Albans Civic Hall. That was how it all started for me. I had just finished cleaning after school.

'Do you want to come and see Thin Lizzy?' my friend and co-worker, Steve Warr, asked. 'My brother, Gary, is going – he'll give us a lift there and back.'

I went along, of course. They had just released the *Night Life* album and they played a lot of tracks from it that night. I stood at the front of the stage, two or three feet in front of them and enjoyed every second of the gig. They had an amazingly exciting electric sound as a live band. I learnt a lot about music from watching and listening to them.

I went on all their early tours, *Night Life, Fighting, Jailbreak, Johnny the Fox*; then the *Live and Dangerous* concerts at Hammersmith, some of which was recorded on my sixteenth birthday, which was the best birthday present ever for me, then the *Bad Reputation* tour, and lastly the *Black Rose* concerts. On record, they were great but 'live' they had an amazingly exciting sound that was then and still is now, unique. On every tour they developed, and it was a special thing to hear and see them.

At the Olympia concert in 1975 I met Brian Robertson, Brian May and Anita Dobson, then Brian Downey, all before the concert where they supported Status Quo. During the concert, Phil Lynott dedicated *Sha-la-la* to me and Steve Warr for giving him a Manchester United scarf. We were both standing right in front of him throughout the concert, cheering the band on. That was on the *Fighting* tour. When they released *Jailbreak* and had a hit single with *The Boys are Back in Town*, we were all so pleased for them because they were such a great band. As songwriters, they had large number of good songs, a great musical style, and a great original sound.

I remember Phil Lynott being interviewed about his success and he said that the idea of it being an overnight success for them was not right. He said that it took a lot of songs and a lot of years to get there. It warms my heart to hear now, all these years later, that bands still acknowledge them with the credit they so rightly deserve.

Anyway, the start of 1986 was not a happy one for a lot of reasons, and Phil Lynott passing away was one of them for me. I needed to move on with my life, because I was really just going nowhere except round and round in circles. That day, I started trying to figure out how to break the cycle once and for all. I ran the risk of going back to being a sofa surfer or a down and out on the streets again if I didn't come up with something this year. So, I contacted the bad boy and the risk taker inside of me; this was done as a last desperate attempt to sort this bad situation out. The only advice from within that part of me was, 'If you could just set yourself up with a bit of trouble and a pinch of shame; just enough embarrassment to stay out of the area on a more permanent basis, you would be able to break free, then head somewhere better.'

I looked for the opportunity, but nothing came up and I did not want to do anything out of order big time as I didn't want to close the door forever. Then, around the middle of 1986, when I had almost resigned myself to being back on the streets as part of my silly life cycle, an opportunity turned up.

A lady friend of Stephen's asked me to babysit. I had agreed to do this, but beforehand I had called round at a friend of a friend's house to pick up, or more correctly, borrow, a tiny diamond ring.

I had bought this ring eight years ago for Colette, my childhood sweetheart, in Garden City town centre for thirty-eight pounds in 1978. I knew it was there, because I had kept a very close track of it since giving it away to Eve, who gave it to her friend Lucy, who then sold it to a guy called John, who gave it to his girlfriend. This was the only ring I have ever bought and it was given back to me by Colette at the request of her new boyfriend, who later became her husband. This was the day after I came back to England from Germany, just over two years before 1986. So, I took the ring from the bowl where it had been kept by the person who now owned it. She was too embarrassed to wear such a cheap declaration of love on her finger, and so only wore it on occasions when no-one would see it. She wanted a much better ring, or should I say a much more expensive declaration of love. I popped it in the purse Kit had given me on her deathbed eighteen months ago. Technically it was theft, and I am ashamed to say that of myself but it is true. John had not told his girlfriend where the ring had come from, but she knew he had bought it fourth hand from Lucy. Hence the reason why it was in a bowl, waiting for that special occasion. Before I went off baby-sitting, I had told John and Brian, our mutual friend, exactly where I was going before I left his flat with my ex-girlfriend's old diamond ring in the purse.

The kids' mother had made sure the three kids were safe and sound in bed when I arrived, checking that they were all fast asleep before she left with Stephen.

Then I waited, and hoped for them to turn up for the ring. From the front window I saw John looking like the angry boyfriend and Brian as his backup, who had been in the flat when I took the ring, come marching down the garden path.

'Where's the ring?' they both said when I opened the door.

I calmly opened the purse that I had all ready for him, and gave him the ring. Then John, followed by Brian, punched and kicked me from the front door through the small hallway, into the kitchen, and then pushed me onto the floor for those last few kicks as they said farewell. Then they left.

I put up about forty percent of blocks to the head punches, but I did not hit back or injure either of them.

Luckily, the kids did not wake up during this silliness. Stephen and the mother of the children returned shortly afterwards. When they found out what had happened, Stephen took me straight round to see John and his girlfriend to mediate my apology for my very bad behaviour. After I had done this, I left that evening and stopped doing the sofa surfing or down and out act for good, as far as I was concerned.

Obviously, the bad boy inside my head wanted a big thank you, as did my inner risk taker, but to be honest I was too embarrassed to even go there, so I moved on as planned. There was no real way of turning back from it all, so it was mission accomplished. This really gave me the push I needed to stay in London and plan my next move to making music.

Everyone was shocked at my behaviour but I am just glad the risk taker got it right and the down and out didn't team up with the bad boy and then sell the ring for a fiver before I had the chance to return it.

I know it was a nasty thing to do, but I had to do something to make my options less attractive there. Luckily for me, this helped me find out later that it was much better being poor in Malvern, than being poor in Hertfordshire or London. I also collected a couple of debts before I left, and so I put some wrongdoings towards me right.

These two particular people wrongly thought I was in no position to do anything about it, so neither of them made any attempt to pay me what I was due. They just didn't think I would ever ask for it back, because I was down and out. One of them owed me for drum equipment and the other one owed me for a car he sold me that he had intentionally bled the brakes on, trying to do me a serious injury, as I found out to my surprise when driving down the Kings Road in Chelsea one sunny afternoon.

So I went to the first one who owed me the money for the drums and asked him if he would pay back the money he owed me.

'No,' he stated, in no uncertain terms.

'Fair enough. Are you sure?' I offered him the opportunity to change his decision.

'Yes. I am sure.'

So he wasn't going to change his mind. I waited for a couple of days, then because I was on the streets, I was out and about early in the morning. I was walking past Turner's house at five a.m. just as he was loading his car to go on a fishing trip with his mates. They saw me.

'Why don't you come with us?' they asked.

'Okay, I will come along,' I replied and got into the back of the car.

After a drive up to Lincolnshire, it must have been around seven-thirty a.m. when we arrived at a remote spot by a river. They got all their gear out of the car and started fishing about a hundred yards away from the car. I hung around for a while watching what they were doing, but not being into fishing, I didn't get involved. Then I spoke to the one who refused to pay me for the drum equipment.

'Hey, Turner, can I borrow your car keys so I can listen to the radio for a bit?' I innocently asked.

He wisely hesitated for a few seconds, then stupidly just gave me the keys. I walked towards the car with the keys in my hand and revenge in my mind as I felt cheated out of the drum equipment when he had refused to pay me. I opened the door of the car, put the keys in the ignition and then I drove it round to the guy who sold me the car with no brakes. He owed me forty pounds for the car and Turner owed me sixty pounds for the drum equipment. So I sold it to him for one hundred pounds cash. When he asked me for the log book, I said Turner had it for him to collect. Then I got a lift from the almost new owner of the car to the train station. Needless to say, they did not take kindly to that style of debt collection, but as I have said many times, here is my address; if you think it was that wrong, come and see me. One word of warning, though, be sure you're waving a big white flag before you knock on my shed door. Otherwise I will consider it a declaration of war and proceed accordingly, fair enough? I am not trying to make out I'm a big tough guy because I am certainly not. However, you best believe me that long gone are the days when I would not react to being treated so badly.

*

After this second romantic fling with the inner bad boy, I went into work hard and play hard mode for the rest of 1986. I started to try harder to make the most of everything. After my twenty-sixth birthday and the leader of the band turning down the Magnet deal without consulting or considering anyone else's opinion in the band, I spent Christmas wandering around the country lanes of 'home sweet home,' Tewin, thinking that somehow next year would be better. I sat on the bench in the graveyard at St. Peter's church around dusk on Christmas day and thought to myself, *What is it you really want to do and what is really achievable in your position?*

The answer was that I wanted to get into a position where I could write and record songs. Even though I kind of knew I had been waiting in vain for things to change with the rock 'n' roll group, and that the old guy in the pub was right, it was difficult to accept that after all the hard work I had put into it in the past couple of years, that now it was not going to go anywhere that great. Especially when the singer who was already wealthy, would say silly things like, 'We should hold out for the big money record contract'.

'Oh, I'm sorry, you should have said. I didn't realise Mick Jagger had a twin brother!' was always something I wanted to say but didn't, when he said such silly things like that.

At these times I would tell my mind not to let the inner 'provocative comedy guy' out of his cage under any circumstances.

*

It was now the start of January 1987. Walking down the Holloway Road every morning to go to work was getting more and more like sucking on an exhaust pipe before doing a day's work in the Royal Northern Hospital, especially after being in Malvern or Tewin for a weekend. Putting up with the congestion and increasingly more polluted city life for seventy-eight pounds a week hardly seemed worth it. This was not any great success to me, neither was chasing rainbows of grand successful rock band ideas but it was a lot better than sleeping rough. I tried to count my blessings rather than dwell on the negatives, as at least I did get to play drums in a band five nights a week or more.

The medical records were now sorted out nicely and my work was becoming much easier now all the records were straight. Now, when a doctor needed a file (eg number 128821), I would just say something like fourth row down, left bottom shelf. Before I had sorted them all out it would take a while to find anything even if you were lucky because a file could be literally anywhere. I felt quite pleased when I had sorted the mess out as did my boss, Mary Gallagher.

New year, fresh start; it was my first day back at work 1987. I walked into the office and Mary greeted me.

'Happy new year, Keythe. I have some good news for you.' She then proceeded to tell me the good news, which was, because I had done such a good job of sorting out the files at The Royal Northern Hospital, there was an offer of promotion for me. They wanted me to consider amalgamating all the records with the Whittington Hospital records up the road. Once this was completed, they wanted all the records put onto computers. She said the post would be starting in a few weeks.

'Okay,' I said, and thought no more of it. There was no mention of a pay increase, which might have been a small incentive for me to see it as a great start to the year. You see, I was an agency staff member from 'Aquarius' at the top of Holloway Road. They got around eight pounds per hour for me, but I only got one pound ninety-five an hour take home pay. Anyway, my work had obviously caught someone's attention, although I was unaware that I was any good at the job because I was too busy enjoying it to notice. I later realised that is why they left me to it, because I was doing such a good job of it.

I had not seen any of the rock 'n' roll group over the Christmas holidays and they were all still away. I was on my own in the house in Archway after my first day back at work. Later that day, I sat down with a pen and paper and wrote out a list of pros and cons. My job at the hospital was going to require a fair amount of commitment from me if I took the new job. There was no guarantee of a decent pay increase and the agency would want to continue getting the lion's share whilst throwing me the scraps.

Then there was the band situation with Paul the singer, who would continue to run things, treating the rest of us like an unpaid backing band. He would continue to sift through my song lyrics while I was at work, then present them slightly altered, claiming them as his own compositions when his songs were equally as good as mine, often even better. It just did not make any sense to me – why could we not just share the joy of writing a good song together?

My first weekend off work in 1987 started on Friday night on 9 January with things still not fully decided in my mind about the direction to take in order to get what I wanted and needed musically. Saturday came and went in a hurry, then on Sunday I met up with a friend from Malvern in South London with a friend of hers from Birmingham. I explained my situation, and told them the record deal story that was really still bugging me. Then I told them that I was finding it hard to develop musically in my present circumstances of being in a band that played only one style of music, even though Matthew, Neil and I had tried many times to convince Paul there was more than one style of music to consider. I knew my desire for creativity was being wasted, and maybe starting from scratch again was my only real sensible option. If I made this move it would enable me to write and then play in whatever style I felt was needed to develop my skills as both a musician and songwriter.

It was now 547 days since I sat watching *Live Aid* in Malvern, and on that day in July 1985, I was a penniless twenty-four-year-old. On this day, Sunday, 11 January, I was twenty-six years old and my situation had not really changed that much. It was now time to seriously change my situation for something better.

On Monday 12 January 1987, I went to Archway got my two drums, two cymbals, song books, poem books, photographs, and tarot cards, then I moved to Malvern.

It was snowing heavily by the time I got to the Cotswolds.

This is going to be tough, but I will work and get myself a better drum kit, a multi-track tape machine and become a writer of songs, regardless of fame or fortune, was what I told myself, when I couldn't even see the road in the blanket of snow. In a strange way it was a bit like changing my life completely all in one go, but at the time I felt it was the only way I could make my desire for song writing and recording happen.

Chapter Five

Who Cares Wins

Over the years I have learnt a lot from people who have helped me in my many hours of need and that is where the idea of 'who cares wins' originates from. If you care about other people and have compassion for those less fortunate than yourself, then you should be happy.

If you are able to spread joy and happiness to those in need, then you should. Too many people have the 'take, take, take,' attitude these days and it is often at the expense of others. This type of selfish action would eventually lead to the downfall of society if it were not irreversible. Fortunately, it is possible to change things and therefore there is a way that could save us all, if we really want it badly enough. The only true way forward is to come together regardless of our differences and to look after each other; it is not a complicated thing, it's a very simple thing to do. The first step is to do something good for someone for free, with no hidden agenda and no strings attached. Then explain to those whom you have helped the simple idea of this, which is that they then pass it on by doing the same good thing free for someone else. The sooner the cynics of caring are dealt with, the better… those groups of people who tend to be better off than you and I and don't see that they should care about anyone else except themselves. The promises of political parties who continually stall progress at the starting blocks by saying that care is at the top of their agenda are meaningless without action. Then, whenever they are criticised, they tell us how urgent it all is for us to do something about it.

Look at the *Live Aid* situation – it was the people of the world who cared enough to help the starving people in Africa, not the politicians or political parties.

Ask yourself the simple question: 'Would I want someone to care for those I love, if I could not do it?' If the answer is yes, then start doing something good for someone… and ultimately yourself, now; no strings attached, for free. If that does not explain the 'Who cares wins' ideal, then perhaps a second example will make things clearer.

The person you love the most in your life is hanging by their fingertips on the edge of a cliff, and they are going to tragically fall to their death. Would you prefer to live in a society that kicks your loved one's fingers away and watches them fall? Or would you prefer to live in a society that saves your loved one, so that you can be happily reunited?

At this stage of human evolution, we are led, divided, and controlled by political parties who profit from the continuation of chaos. After all, politics has become a game of blame whilst creating problems for the poor, like a 'job creation scheme.'

*

So, I had moved to Malvern. I had a place to stay and the rent was cheap. I was sharing with three other people who were all vegetarians, so I joined the club and lasted seven years on my first attempt. I certainly found it good for my health, which is something I always need to be mindful of.

I realised pretty quickly that there were a hell of a lot of people with mental health issues in the area. This was due to the fact that the two large local asylums were in the process of releasing and relocating people into the community.

The Care in the Community Act was either on paper, or on its way to being implemented from paper. It was in fact both, but these things often have a delay between what is written and what it is actually possible to provide without a lot of organising.

I spent many evenings learning about the history of the area's asylum hospitals spelt out to me in detail over a meal and a few bottles of wine from people who had worked there. Many of them had witnessed the horrors first-hand in their years of service in and around the asylums.

Now at this time there were a lot of people being placed in the community from the local asylum hospital with very inadequate support.

*

There was a television documentary made about this local asylum hospital, which stood on the hilly ground between Malvern and Worcester. The programme exposed some of the practices that went on there.

One of the psychiatrists who had worked there appeared in the documentary and spoke openly about some of the various treatments. His confidence surprised me and he certainly had no remorse for his participation in these 'therapies', let alone any feelings for those who had been left in a much worse state in the community after his and his medical colleagues' administrations. Then he revealed why he was able to speak so openly in a documentary and with such a lack of concern for those people the asylum had left in turmoil.

All of the recorded evidence of medication administration and other 'therapies' that were carried out there had been burnt in the hospital incinerator on site before the closure of the asylum. This cemented the very tragic stories in the documentary from some of the former patients, who gave first-hand accounts of what they went through and said they still suffered from the side effects of medications and therapies to this day. They now have absolutely no chance of any kind of justice.

So I came into contact with a lot of people who needed a lot of help with mental health issues, and quite a lot of their problems had been caused by drug induced psychoses.

This asylum hospital was where, for several decades, various 'doctors of the mind' experimented on people, mainly with electric shock treatment and LSD. Many people were sent there by local GPs for help; hard to believe now but a very true story back then. Housewives with depression or people who just did not feel too well would be advised to go there and try the 'therapy' at the hospital. GPs made it easy for people to access it by laying on a bus service that would pick them up from their homes or local bus stops, then transport them to the hospital. The large, dark Victorian hospital was encircled by a very high barbed wire fence. This was to prevent the more seriously ill patients, who could be a danger to themselves and others, from escaping. There was a double gate at the front entrance for extra security that only opened when the other had closed. Once the day patients were there, they would be given a dose of pure liquid LSD and then taken into secure units or rooms, depending on their reaction to the therapy. If a day patient had a severe reaction and appeared to be a high risk, then they would be strapped to a bed or put into a padded cell. Some patients would spend the eight-hour day simply hallucinating quietly in a corner, or wandering aimlessly around the secure unit.

The day patients were kept separate from those who resided there semi-permanently. They were therefore not able to access the outside spaces and mix with the more severely ill patients. Around five p.m. the day patients would be given another large dose of medicine that would reduce the hallucinations significantly although, for some this was inadequate, and they would suffer the effects of the LSD for many years afterwards. Then they would be transported home.

This practice went on for decades and many people who simply went to their doctors for mild depression or other minor complaints, ended up living with years of horrific mind-altering drug-induced side effects. All this was done in the name of 'Therapy,' until the hospital was closed down in the late 1980's.

*

The seriousness of it all did not really sink in with me at first, the matter being very complex to deal with, let alone understand. That all changed when I met a lady who would often stop me in the street and ask me for cigarettes in a desperate manner. Her name was Gene and back then, thirty odd years ago, I smoked *Silk Cut* cigarettes. Whenever she asked me I would give her a few cigarettes at a time, because she was clearly in need. Then she would tell me how kind I was.

'No problem,' I would say.

You could easily see from the chronic tobacco stains on her fingers that she was a really serious smoker. After meeting her a few times out and about, she opened up to me, and told me she had been let out into the community from the local asylum hospital. She had been allocated a flat down the road, although she spent most of her days on the streets, begging. She said she had a social worker who did not provide enough support. However, at this time there were so many people needing support, the visits from social workers were short and sweet because their workloads were far too heavy.

I was working at the Malvern Arts Workshop. This soon became the meeting place and work place for a lot of people who had been relocated into the community from the two asylums. One was north of Malvern; the other, south, so to say I was in the middle of it all at that time, is an understatement indeed.

To me, these were people who had real problems; they made me realise how lucky I really was. I had survived some hardships in my life, but the things that I thought were problems were nothing compared to what I was seeing and hearing from these people. Some were unmarried women who had fallen pregnant and then been locked up in asylums for forty years. There was one man who stole a push bike and was also locked away for forty years. Another example was a man who was seen vacantly staring at someone quite unintentionally. He ended up being locked away, from his teenage years to his mid-forties. His incarceration included being locked in a padded cell, and given electric shock treatment and LSD therapy over many years. These were just a few of the horror stories that were the lives of these people so far. Once they were rehoused into the community, they had to put up with being treated badly at times by those in the community who simply refused to accept them as humans.

A couple of elderly ladies who were friends of mine from the Malvern Arts Workshop, had dog mess posted through their letter box on a regular basis. Some members of the general public would call them horrible names, and they would often be overcharged when out shopping, because they had never had money before this time of their new-found freedom.

People would find out where they lived and then rob them. This was the late eighties and early nineties – the very time when the Care in the Community Act was being talked about with great pride by people who were being paid to help these less fortunate people to cope with the very serious issues in their lives. The real problem of the 'care act' and its provision was that these people did not just have problems that occurred Monday to Friday, nine a.m. to five p.m., they all needed support twenty-four seven, all year round. Helping others then became a large part of my life and was something I did wherever, whenever and for whoever, as much as I possibly could. This was a job that had found me. I did not in any way intend to end up doing this, but I could not walk away from these people when they clearly needed help. I knew I could defend them and help them, so I did just that without giving it a second thought.

In the thirty odd years that I have been of service to those who need support, I do find it hard when I hear people say, 'It must be rewarding.' That throw-away phrase only serves to make me think it is a way in which some people prefer to really say,

'Rather you than me'.

Now, in 2020, thanks to the Italians who did it first, people clap the NHS staff and keyworkers like myself, on their doorsteps during this man made Coronavirus pandemic. After doing the job I have done for thirty odd years without this kind of appreciation, I would rather people used our work as an example. Then, instead of clapping to show their support, it would be better if they did something good for someone who needs it. Just give yourself a chance to be selfless for a moment; think how much better the world would become if people really cared for those in real need and helped those truly less fortunate souls. That would be a better way of showing true gratitude to the health care sector, benefiting yourself and your loved ones in the long term.

*

Back to my job working at the Malvern Arts Workshop. One bitterly cold day in early 1988, the outside water pipes to the café had frozen and no amount of caustic soda would unblock them.

So I was at the back of the building, burning planks of wood next to the frozen downpipes, trying to unfreeze them at the request of the boss of the workshops. Suddenly, Gene turned up, shouting to me and asking desperately if I could help her.

'The vicar had sex with me for cigarettes and now won't give me them! Can you help me? He's in the shop next door now, can you get them from him? Please!'

Confused and more than a little shocked, I thought she must be mistaken.

'Sure, Gene, I will help you, show me the vicar,' I said.

We went next door to the newsagents. Sure enough, there was a man inside at the counter who looked like a vicar, wearing a tweed jacket with elbow patches, a dog collar, and a gold crucifix on a chain. He was just turning to leave the shop.

As he came outside. Gene shouted, 'That's him! Give me my cigarettes!'

'Excuse me, Vicar,' I ventured, 'this lady says you owe her cigarettes?'

He stared at me, frowning. 'No, I don't. You must have the wrong person,' he said and walked off.

'You had sex with me, and I want my cigarettes!' Gene shouted.

He did not look back as he walked off briskly down the hill.

'Gene, come into the café and I will make you a cup of tea,' I said.

She came into the café and I made her a drink. While she was having her tea, I went next door to the newsagent and spoke to Tina, the lady who worked there, about the vicar. She knew all about it and told me that the man who was dressed as a vicar was not a real vicar.

'He is an ex-asylum patient who dresses as a vicar, who does have sex with Gene and sometimes pays her in cigarettes.' Tina said.

So Gene was telling the truth. I bought her a pack of twenty cigarettes, went back to the café and gave them to her.

She was very anxious and smoking dog-ends when I returned to her.

'Look,' I said kindly, 'in future if you need cigarettes, come and find me, and stay away from the vicar. Okay?'

After that day, Gene would be waiting for me to give her a couple of cigarettes most mornings outside the café. I think she did stay away from the 'vicar' after that day.

Sadly, though, as was often the case with these unwanted souls, Gene passed away alone in her flat where she did not like being alone, some years later. It took a few weeks before she was discovered, when a neighbour noticed that the milk deliveries outside her front door were mounting up to several weeks' worth. Sadly, the 'Care in the Community Act' was more of an 'act' than real care. Health and social care workers were given very large caseloads, which were not really possible to complete, leaving people like Gene lonely and highly vulnerable. This left an ocean of people with similar problems, who were extremely confused and alone in the community.

They had gone from being supported twenty-four seven for decades, to having a one-hour visit in every three hundred and thirty-six hours – a fortnight. On top of this, they had to contend with the side effects from years of being pumped full of hallucinogens and many, many other 'experimental medicines'.

This issue was very largely overlooked before, during and after the implementation of the Care in the Community Act. The focus was instead placed on how much better off they would be in the community, which was undeniably true. However, this should not have been used to ignore the historical medical facts, or destroy them in the hospital incinerator. Just to even begin to understand what these people had to endure in these asylums for years on end is unimaginable. It would make what we now hold up as 'abusive practice' seem like a drop in the ocean compared to being experimented on with mind altering drugs. However, by all the first-hand accounts of the staff I spoke with, there was a culture that turned a blind eye to the most horrific abuses.

The shock of being placed into the community in the late eighties, after being locked away for decades, was extremely hard for them to adjust to. Not to mention the changes that society and the world had undergone whilst they were being experimented on in the name of 'Medical Progress'.

The Malvern Arts Workshop started as an unofficial and unpaid part of the care in the community programme, and then soon became an integral part of it. Suddenly, it was seen as a highly investable project by the local Health Authority who used it to smooth out some of the very rough edges and shortcomings the act had produced.

The Malvern Arts Workshop was a very large split-level building. It was in the middle of a row of shops that had living quarters at the rear, top, and bottom. It had three kitchens, three bathrooms and one main large shopfront that was used as a café, then an area for art exhibitions from all over the UK Some local artists also sold art and craft items there, on a sale or return basis. Downstairs, there were meeting rooms that doubled up as a cinema room, there was also a pottery room, art room, printing room and a photography room. At the very end of it all there was a cellar room which I rented to live in and used as a music recording studio for ten years.

The café upstairs sold mainly vegetarian meals, cakes, and puddings, all made on site from scratch by two main cooks and numerous kitchen assistants, including myself. Light refreshments were also sold in the café, which was open seven days a week, and I worked there every day from eight a.m. until six p.m. I was always the first person in there to set up the salads and soup bases. Then, at the end of the day, I was the last person there, scrubbing the kitchen floors and then the hallways, on my hands and knees, until some time later, when the owner bought a mop and bucket. Last job of the day was to hoover the café and art exhibition area. I was paid eight pounds per day from January 1987 to April 1989, which I declared to the job centre, weekly. They made the appropriate deductions to my supplementary benefits. I did not claim housing benefit as I paid my own rent at the house I shared until May 1988 when, following a disagreement, I moved into the cellar music room.

The money I earned in the café I had saved and managed to buy a Black Pearl six piece export drum kit, second hand, for six hundred and fifty pounds. Then I saved up and bought a pair of 14 inch Ziljian new beat hi-hats, a 19 inch Ziljian ride and a 16 inch Ziljian crash. After a lot of hard work, I had half decent drum kit for the first time in five or six years. I then saved up again and brought a Roland Juno 60 keyboard. Part of my unwritten rental agreement was that I would teach and give drumming instruction very cheaply at two to four pounds per hour, to bring in more costumers to the Arts Workshop. I had to rent out the music room to local music groups at the very cheap rate of four pounds per four-hour session. This meant I had to move my stuff out every time, and then back in at the end of every rental, but it helped me to pay the rent. By the time I was renting the music room, I had been trying to play drums properly for about fourteen years. I understood how to read music; this was something that I had already been taught at secondary school by my music teacher, Mrs. Britten, who was Benjamin Britten's sister. I only wish I had paid more attention in lessons and I would have done, if only she could have stopped telling me how famous her brother was, which made me all dreamy. It was great, hearing all his music in class, though.

*

The Malvern Arts Workshop were producing a promotional leaflet to introduce the services available and I reluctantly agreed to be listed as a 'Drum Instructor'. Even though this was not entirely true because I was not a drum instructor. However,

I went along with it. The choice was the unspoken type where you either agree, or risk the unwritten rental agreement being revoked and given to someone else who would agree with various terms and conditions. The next thing I knew, I had a photographer taking pictures of me playing the drums in the music room, for a newspaper article on the services available at the Arts Workshop, one of which was my 'Drum Instruction'.

The article in the local newspaper passed without much fuss. Then a couple of weeks later, in early February, I was in the music room writing a song when a young lady came in and asked if I could play some music for her group. She explained that she had been looking for someone to play music as an activity for a group of disabled people. I was not entirely sure what this entailed, but I said that I could do it anyway. Then she left, saying she would call back sometime the following week and sort out the details with me. When she had gone, I thought no more of it because I got a lot of people showing interest who then failed to follow up on their initial enquiries.

The following week, I was writing in my break time from the café upstairs as I often did, and I was down there trying to improve my song-writing skills when the same lady popped her head round the door.

'Is it okay if we come in?' she asked.

Curious, I replied, 'Yes, come in.'

There were five people in all – two staff members, two young men who did not speak, and a young lady who spoke the same words over and over. She began asking me questions, which I tried to answer, but could not quite finish before she asked me another question. Then there was the lady who had made enquiries last week – her name was Angela and she had also bought her boss, Irene, with her.

Irene was the manager of a local residential home that cared for twenty-two special needs adults. All the residents had severe mental and physical disabilities. The group looked around the cellar room but apart from the drum kit and the Roland keyboard, there was nothing much else to see. It was not long before they asked if I could come to the residential home and do a music session.

'Yes, I can do that,' I agreed. 'What time and where?'

'Priory Road at eleven a.m. Friday, third of March.' (1989)

'Great, see you then,' I said, and they left.

It never occurred to me at the time that when they had seen the Roland keyboard in the music room, they would assume that I could play the piano.

When I arrived there on that Friday morning, I was greeted by the sight of a very large Victorian House, inside which was a spacious front room where they had an upright piano. I was taken to it on arrival. There were a dozen people in the room with various disabilities – or abilities – depending on which way you looked at it.

I had never seen or heard anything like it before; my being there seemed to have caused a ripple of vocalising. It could have been my imagination or simply what normally happened whenever a new person came into the home. Soon after I arrived, I was introduced to each person. I tried to engage them with eye contact, whilst telling them who I was and why I was there. Some of them verbally engaged with me and made eye contact. Those people who did not verbally engage with me because they were vocally impaired all seemed to respond with their eyes, or in other physical ways with gestures.

Once the introductions had been completed, the Manager opened the upright piano and gave me four piano music books. Three were classical and one was a rock 'n' roll songbook. As I sat down at the piano, I thought I had best mention that I was a drummer and that I didn't really play the piano that well. Then I looked through the rock 'n' roll book, desperately trying to find something to play but there was nothing I could confidently have a go at. While I was doing this urgent searching, Angela and Irene were handing out various percussion instruments to the group of people. By then, on the very last two pages, I found an easy version of the Chubby Checker hit, *Let's Twist Again*. I checked with the group that they were ready, and they all seemed good to go. Then I hit the C major chord to signal a two-bar count in, and away we went. The people went wild! Big time. They were screaming, shouting and jumping up and down. At some points in the session, percussion instruments were launched at speed across the room, bouncing off furniture and various walls behind me. Then this one very excited young man called Andrew came round the right-hand side of me and started hitting random high notes at the end of the piano. This was so brilliant because it was covering up all the mistakes I was making!. Then he did a spinning dance on one leg and started making noises like an American Indian ready to go into battle. This was followed by bouncing up and down, waving his hands in the air, and making growling noises. Then back to hitting random notes on the piano. No staff member dared to stop him, because he would have hit them if they tried to stop him or the music. The same song went on for about thirty minutes. During this time, I noticed that they all followed the music. When the piano was played loud, they got loud, when I played quietly, they became quiet with it, and when it went wild, they went really wild.

This enabled me to make the music a journey for them, like a safe fairground ride, and they loved it. The music could induce the thrilling feeling of an exciting ride without leaving the room.

When we had finished the session, I was confident they would now understand that I was not a piano player by any stretch of the imagination, then they would politely thank me for doing the session and I would be on my way. So I was very surprised when, afterwards, they asked me when I could come back and do it again. I was a little unprepared for that request.

'Same time next week?' I said, without giving it a second thought. What was I thinking… because this was not going to further my career as a songwriter, or a musician. Then the Manager told me how Edward Elgar had played for the people in the asylums years ago. I think she told me this true story to encourage me in some way. Then she said they would like to pay me five pounds for my time, as they knew I would have to take two hours off from working in the café to do the sessions there. I accepted the offer because that was more than half a day's pay for me at the café, so over the next two months I did five more sessions. There were two sessions that I missed because I was needed at the café.

At the last session in April, a lady from head office turned up and offered me a job. The job was a full-time post as an Activity Unit Organiser Assistant. Angela would be my main boss and we would do the daycare activities for the twelve people in the music group. Some of the twelve attended a daycare centre locally and so this meant we would have eight people on average per day to engage in whatever activities they liked to do. Doing personal care was something that bothered me but after I overcame my initial concerns about it, I was fine, and I accepted the job the following week.

Previously to my taking this job, it had been done by a nun called Sister Jeanette. In the interview for the job, after they had confirmed with me that I did not take drugs, would stick the job and had no criminal record, they asked me if there was anything I would like to ask them. I requested a verbal agreement from them that the group would be free to make films, music, and art. These were to be shown, performed, and displayed for sale. They agreed to this so long as I found the funds to do these projects. Then once we had discussed the way in which I would do this, through fund raising and using my own money, they agreed. I started my new activity unit job on 01 May 1989. Now I worked there in the daytime, and at Malvern Arts Workshop in the evenings and at weekends.

I also started doing some nights shifts in the music room, recording and writing my songs. This often depended on my work schedule.

It may have been just a strange coincidence that I had replaced a nun at my new job. However, when I first lived in Malvern, two years previous to getting this job, I had regular visits from a nun called Sister Elizabeth, who resided at the local convent. She seemed to know about me before we became friends, but she never said how that was so.

*

At work, I borrowed a small video camera and experimented with the group, taking various dramatic shots. We did shots of objects falling out of the windows at the home, and a young lady called Honour dressed in a sheet, standing in the garden like a statue. Angela and I set up a timetable which contained art sessions, drama, sports, swimming, speech and language therapy, co-ordination sessions, music sessions, recording sessions, and outings to various places of interest. We filled every moment we could with activities that our group enjoyed and would benefit from doing physically, mentally, and spiritually.

I bought myself a Tascam four track portable studio with my first month's wage packet for four hundred pounds through my friend, Paul White, who was editor of *Home Recording* at the time, which later became *Sound on Sound*. This is really how I got going with recording my songs on an industrial scale night and day, all thanks to Paul.

That sunny summer's evening after work when I walked up the hill with my new multi-track tape machine, I suddenly had a sense of great joy and optimism for my musical future. Only two years before this, I had nothing. Now I had an electric guitar, a Roland keyboard, a decent drum kit and now a multi-track recorder.

This progress made all the hard work seem worth it. For the first time in a long while, I had something to show for all the work that I had done and I felt like I was getting somewhere with what I had initially intended to do when I moved to Malvern. I started recording all the songs I had been writing straight away so, every day as soon as my daytime work was done, I would start recording and playing.

Angela and I raised about a thousand pounds and then bought a Panasonic SVHS video camera so that the group could start making films.

I wrote *Astroman* as our first film, which is a story about an astronaut who is sent into the future to find a cure for the food and water plague on earth. When he returns many years later, the world is controlled by a new leader who wants the cure for himself. The story came to me at a time when Chernobyl had not long blown up, and the trees at the start of the film are all damaged. I felt there was a distinct difference in the health of the tall Christmas trees in Little Switzerland on the west hills; they all looked as if they had been very badly damaged. In my opinion, something was wrong and my beanie went from black to red that year.

I used my own money for videotapes and costumes. Then when I started filming, I did the editing live as we went along on board the camera itself, so we had to live with whatever film we took on any given day, or rewind very carefully and do another take. I spent many evenings looking through the film parts using the tiny eye piece and doing the voice-overs on the four-track. Then once this was done, I created the music and sent it straight to the camera as the completed soundtrack. It was a primitive cheap method that was incredibly hard to do, but it worked out good in the end. We premièred the film at the Malvern Fringe Festival 1990. As a support act to the film, we played some music to a film I had made; the whole music support act to the feature film lasted eleven minutes.

It had never been done before by a group with such severe disabilities, but we played a lot of music together, so we were well rehearsed. I played the Roland Juno 60, Andrew did his spinning on one leg, playing the hand drum. He also did his vocal noises and growling whilst spinning at the same time. Michael played a DD 10 Yamaha drum machine; Elaine played drum kit; Crispen played shaker; Mike played tambourine; John played hand drum, and Cheryl leaned on me saying, 'Hello!'

while I was trying to play the keyboard.

The other members of our group watched in the sold-out audience and the film went down really well with the whole audience, all forty seven minutes of it. My music composing advisor and piano teacher, Robert Norris, was there and after the showing he said, he thought it was 'musically interesting'. I was happy with that as he is a master musician himself who has answered thousands of my musical questions over the years and taught me very well how to use my ears and listen when composing music.

I took this as a really good sign, which instantly made me think that we could have made a decent impression on the local newspaper. The review for the *Malvern Gazette* was lovely, when Ben Wilmott said, 'It just goes to show what disabled people can achieve when given the chance.'

We were paid one hundred pounds for the whole thing and the group chose to spend sixty pounds of the money on a boat trip down the river Severn from Upton. The other forty pounds we used towards the costs of our next film, *Money Mad*. This is a story about a man called Robert Smith who has lots of different jobs, then he wins a talent show as a comedian, with a joke I borrowed from Eddie Murphy. After he wins the prize money of ten thousand pounds he goes home and falls asleep, and while sleeping, he has a dream that he is in a band. This film gave us a platform to use all of our art and music in the content of the film. The money in the film that was thrown around like confetti was my savings. The artworks were the group's work that had been created in art sessions at the Malvern Arts Workshop. The music was all made by us in jam sessions and recording sessions. The cello music at the start of the film was called *Rain on the Pavement*. It was my first attempt at writing a proper music score and was played by Vivian Norris with me playing the background strings. The closing song was done by myself, and sound on sound editor, Paul White, with voice samples from each member of the group. At the end of the film, the guitarist of the band, Mr. Diamond Guitar Jones tricks Robert and takes his winnings to America. It has a happy ending though because, in reality, Robert was still asleep and only dreaming.

We also premièred this film at the Malvern Fringe Festival in 1991, the year after *Astroman*. It was very well received and earned another good review in the local paper. After this project, Angela moved to Germany with her husband and I carried on with the group.

We took on a new helper, a volunteer called Helen Vockins. She had great artistic ideas and skills in art. We set about making our third and final film, *The Magic Machine*, a story about a machine that could control people's minds. We did a lot more with locations in this film, branching out into areas we had not used before. We did, however, use one location in all three films and that was Whitley Court. Bob Dylan used a picture of himself standing there by one of the columns for the cover of his *Blonde on Blonde* album. The place has a great atmosphere, considering it is just a massive burnt out building where the fire claimed all of it, except for the church at the side of the house, which is beautiful. Edward Elgar's father played there a lot whenever he was repairing the church organ.

Sadly, the Malvern Fringe Festival could not find a slot for us once this film had been completed, due to the change of trustees who thought having people with disabilities was not a very financially sound idea, and so it was never seen by the public. The group and I, along with those who appeared in the film, enjoyed one private showing.

We had had a great time making all of the films and we had made our point, which was that instead of saying people with disabilities should be able to do this or that, we just did it instead of merely talking about it. It made a big difference to the people involved and although it was expensive for me to do, the results were amazingly positive. These sorts of activities should be made available to more groups, because of the benefits of their inclusiveness.

✳

Most nights I would spend in the music room writing songs, then I would play and record them. I would send out demos of these songs all the time to different people, and hoped to get a lucky break, but I never did. A decent manager who understood how to achieve this would have helped, I guess. The songs were either not good enough or just didn't end up in the right place at the right time. It was 1993 and I just wanted a decent job, writing songs or playing drums for someone. I tried to fill my time with musical activities, hoping this would stop me from thinking too much about ancient history, pyramids and the Nazca Lines. There was not much information available on the Nazca Lines back then that I had not already read or looked at over and over again.

At this time I had two main jobs and worked seven days a week, I did a nine to five activity unit job with mentally and physically disabled people from Monday to Friday, and I would do some weekday evenings at The Malvern Arts Workshop as well as all day and evening on a Saturday, followed by Sunday daytime.

I usually had Sunday evenings off, although I never had holidays away anywhere. If I was off work from my activity unit job, I would write and record songs in the cellar music room. It was at this time that I began to re-read all my archaeology books to try and see if I had overlooked anything useful.

I would sometimes get books from Peg, from far-away places, about ancient cultures or religious themes, like the *Teachings of Buddha*. She would tell me amazing things about her travels across the globe. This was obviously something I would have liked to have done myself, but my main concern was working to keep a roof over my head, as I could not afford to end up homeless again.

I visited Dad in London a lot during these times. He would cook delicious food for us, and we would talk. 'Drum for me now, Keat,' was something he would often say to me. Anyway, I would drum on whatever there was available, and Dad would listen. He just loved the fact that I played musical instruments, and whenever we were out he would very proudly bring it up in conversations with his friends.

'My son, Keat, him play whole heap of music and him have job. Him is a righteous man, see.' Not many people Dad mixed with worked for a living, so it was something I would frequently hear him say. He was proud of me for staying out of trouble and also that I worked hard for a living. However, it was never easy going into Dad's world and ignoring how bad it was at times; it was often very difficult to be around that sort of culture.

*

In January 1993, I started learning karate properly, being trained by military service men which included a lot of SAS and ex-SAS. I trained in Hereford, Malvern, Birmingham and London every week, wherever the courses and training was held.

My three main training sessions were in Malvern on Tuesdays and Sundays, then on Friday nights in Hereford. They taught me karate and various other forms of self-defence which gave me a great amount of discipline and helped my mind, body and spirit. What they gave me through their expert teaching and training changed my life completely. What I did not know at the time – between January 1993 and December 1999 when I was full on training – was that I was not just learning how to fight; I was learning how to best use my mind. I am forever grateful to them for helping me through some very difficult and challenging times.

I even had an award for being a good student from my main instructor, Sensei Clifford. The award was a calligraphy writing by Master Funakoshi Hatsun Jindo which reads, *Parting the clouds, seeking the way.*

Learning the art of karate and self-defence with them made me very focused on my music, especially my drumming. It also gave me the confidence to stick up for myself and for the vulnerable people I cared for in my daily work.

Maybe a coincidence or just one of those funny things that happen in life was that my main instructor and his instructor used to train across the road in the Holy Trinity Church hall. Now and again, I would see them sitting in the café, drinking tea. At the time I thought they were either undercover policemen or some kind of agents, and I was right.

My karate training ended abruptly after seven years, on Tuesday 21 December 1999 when my Achilles tendon snapped. I had been hit on my Achilles by an electric wheelchair which had caused it to rupture the week before, then a few kicks at training did the rest, later that day. I continue to practice what they taught me to this day, as it is super good for my health. My main instructor, Sensei Clifford, will always want to show me his super advanced skills in some way and I am always happy to learn something new, especially if I can come away uninjured. There really is nothing like it. I had served a lot of famous people food and drinks in the Malvern Arts Workshop over the years, especially actors and musicians. Black Sabbath Drummer, Bill Ward, was a regular. I ended up recording music and writing with some of them, like the guitarist, Gary Roberts, of *The Boomtown Rats*, a few years after *Live Aid*.

So, I was working seven days a week, doing karate three times a week, then writing songs, playing a lot, and recording. I would play all the instruments and then get various ladies to speak certain phrases and use their recorded voices in samples on the songs. I would aim to express certain things like love, loss and other popular or obscure themes.

I wrote rock songs, pop songs, relaxation music, music for the garden, music for the bath, rain songs, love songs, classical music, instrumentals and theme tunes. In 1994, I started what was to be my most ambitious music project, entitled, *X-ism*. A year later, it became *Ex-ism*. Then I toyed with the idea of calling it *The Lost T-shirts of Atlantis* but in the end settled with *The Lost Chords Of Atlantis*.

When I started writing this collection of nineteen songs, I used background string movements to link them all together. On top of the strings in between each song, I used samples of people talking about the life and times of Jimi Hendrix. Then I asked a friend of mine, Riche K, to record the space chat from NASA live, and added that to the interludes and songs. At the time, Peg had insisted that there was going to be a woman on the space station who was going to attempt to become pregnant up there. When I listened to what they were saying it did not mention anything like that directly, but they most likely would not mention sensitive information. They did say certain things like 'Test point 11-A' and talk about growing food up there; also the evolutionary process, building on what has come before and everything that comes after. That could have been something to do with getting pregnant in space.

Whenever I hear people doing space chat up there, I always wonder how good it would be, taking a closer look at the ancient sites from above. Many ancient legends contain accounts of people in the past having the ability to fly, either on their own or in crafts of one kind or another. If we were to end our civilisation now and there was only a handful of survivors, they may well produce written accounts of human produced objects that flew through the skies. Then future generations of people would ponder the question of an advanced civilisation on earth in the past, like we do now about the past.

✳

I started recording *The Lost Chords Of Atlantis* tapes in late February 1995 and finished it in November 1997. The last song on the CD, *Gimmicks*, I recorded in 1999 and it became the last track. This music project, especially the NASA part, drew me back into full-on research into the Nazca Lines and I got a new map. This contained half of the main lines at Nazca and I spent long periods of time reading research papers that various people had put online. This served to make me realise that I needed a better grasp of the history basics in order to move forward. I read up on what Charles Hapgood had said about earth crust displacement and the shifting polar ice caps.

Then I read his *Maps of the Ancient Sea Kings, Evidence of Advanced Civilization in the Ice Age*. This book gave me hope that there actually was something undiscovered to look for. However, it was difficult to fully understand so it was one step at a time.

✶

In 1997, a lot changed for me. I lost someone I loved at the beginning of February, so I was grieving privately for a very long time.

In March, from the evening of the eighteenth I started hanging round with the violin virtuoso, Nigel Kennedy and his friend, singer/songwriter, Caleb Clarke. It was such a refreshing break for me; we had a lot of laughs while I learnt a lot about music from Nigel and Caleb. Nigel had just released his Rockfield's CD masterpiece, *Kafka*, and the sounds he got from the violin in those recordings are truly amazing! Anyway, it was great to make music with them both, for the sheer joy of making music. There was a lot of nonsense that was being bandied around at the time in music, when every CD that was released started with the title 'Greatest ever… this or that'. Every release suggested that there was never going to be anything better in our lifetime, ever. Why didn't they just say 'Greatest hits so far', which would be so refreshing? But I guess those titles were decided by record executives who wanted to drain every last drop from their artists before dumping them.

Anyway, I learnt a lot from Nigel about music and what the music business is really like at the higher levels. As for fame, he put it very simply.

'When you're famous, everybody wants something,' he said.

When I gave Nigel a copy of *The Lost Chords of Atlantis* in December 1997, he listened to it.

'There are some magic moments on it,' was what he said about it. That was the best compliment on my music I have ever had, and coming from the world's best violinist, made it all the more memorable. This was around January 1998 and previously to this, in April 1997, I had found a new map of the western part of the Nazca lines on the internet. I made a load of copies and displayed them everywhere in the cellar so that I could meditate on them while I searched them for clues as to what they really were. I carried a small version in my wallet at all times so that if I had any spare moments, I could study them for the answer.

All this took me through 1997 and I had side one of *The Lost Chords Of Atlantis* professionally transferred from tape to CD by Mr. Zimmerman, who had put an advert in *Sound on Sound*. I was very pleased with the result when I received the CDs in the post. I sent one copy home to my friends in Tewin.

By the end of the first quarter of 1998, The Malvern Arts Workshop had come to an end due to the owner of the business and the trustees not seeing the same future for the project. This left only me in the building that was being sold or leased to a new owner, who wanted me out. Before I left, I wrote all my notes on part two, which I had recorded in 1996-1997, then I mixed it and put the finishing touches to my final work there, *The Lost Chords Of Atlantis*.

I was the last man standing, then one day I walked outside the building where I was greeted by a large red estate agent's sign that said SOLD. So, after twelve years of hard work, it was suddenly and unceremoniously gone.

Nigel knew what had happened and was supportive of me at this time. We spent many magical nights playing and listening to great music, wherever we were at the time. This was how I learnt that a musical phrase played on an instrument can be highly developed over a very long period of time. For instance, I had heard Nigel play parts of *Sweet and Slow* from his 2013 *Recital* CD many times. So this method helped me to understand how to develop my own ideas and songs over long periods of time. Everyone does it, but it's knowing that you are doing it that helps you to monitor your progress.

*

At some point in 1997, I transferred the Nazca lines to a map of the world, and they ran from Easter Island to somewhere off the east coast of Japan. I did not notice at the time that this was just over halfway round the world. Two years before this, in 1995, I was exploring the idea that during the great flood, many coastal sites would have been taken by the sea, never to return. Today, we are constantly told that sea levels will rise with global warming and then coastal areas will again be consumed by the sea. If history repeats itself, then perhaps so does the fact that what will come has already been, including great floods. It should be no surprise that structures have been found all over the world not far from the coasts of various places, most notably the underwater structures off the coast of Yonaguni Island. This is extremely close to where the western part of the Nazca Lines end, when enlarged to a world size scale. These lines across the world map was just a theory and so I couldn't seriously put it forward as an amazing discovery, so I continued to search for the big one, 'the indisputable discovery'.

Chapter Six

The lottery Experience

I had achieved a lot from working with people with disabilities. The money I had made from that and other various jobs were the fuel for my simple, safe, steady existence. As far away as possible from where I had started in life, maybe some would see it as being in a boring bubble, but not being homeless was my top priority. More importantly, though, was that my wages funded all of my creative projects. All of the work I did was so that I could continue to fund research on my own terms into my music, artistic works and my research into the Nazca Lines.

It was 1997 and just over twelve years since Peter had crashed the van into the wall on the West Malvern Road in May 1985, the day I first arrived in Malvern to play in The Malvern Fringe Festival. I had now been working here for the last twelve years.

Now it was many years after I had first read the quote in the *I Ching Book of Changes* and then put the book back on Stephen's bookshelf. I had not seen or heard from Stephen for over a decade; we had lost touch. Then Eve, a mutual friend of ours, told me he was in Holland, running a bar. That sounded like a Stephen possibility to me. Anyway, I was roughly a hundred miles away from the bookshelf where I had replaced the book after reading it all those years ago.

One evening in early 1997, I decided to visit the lady who had booked us to play The Lamb in The Malvern Fringe Festival all those years ago, for a catch up. I had recently seen her out and about, and she had expressed an interest in hearing some of my new classical music that I had written and recorded. I went round to her house, where we drank tea and listened to the music I had recently made. Then she had a phone call and left the room. I stood up to stretch my legs, and wandered over to her bookshelf to check out her reading material. At first, I thought I was seeing things and tilted my head, taking a closer look. Sure enough, I was not seeing things, it was Stephen's copy of the *I Ching Book of Changes*, with a slight tear in the cover. Could I be mistaken? I opened the book and went to the pages where I had used a pencil to write notes to myself. There I found my pencil-written note on the page next to the interesting section that I had intended to re-read.

I was holding the book in my hand when the lady came back into the room.

'Where did you get this book from?' I had to ask.

She went pale, seeing what book I had in my hand, firstly looking at the book then looking at the space on the shelf. Then in her best innocently high-pitched girlie voice, she said she was not sure where she got it from. Losing eye contact at the same time as saying this, she knew full well that she told me she had once been in Stephen's flat alone. She had waited there for him although she left before he returned, all those years ago, and borrowed the book without his permission. Suddenly all flustered, she waved her hands at me in a dismissive manner.

'You can have it back. I mean take it, if you want it!' she said, still waving her hand as if to be rid of me with the book.

I thanked her for the tea and listening to the music, then I left with the book. It was what Stephen would have wanted. However, it had now been returned so no harm was done. So, until I saw Stephen again and returned it to him, this reunion was meant to be. He taught me that karmic lesson as a matter of fact, and I know he would be laughing if he knew about this situation; I'm sure of that.

*

At this time, I would get the odd phone call from Peg now and again but that was about it. Unless I went to visit people down in Garden City, I didn't hear from them much at all. That was all about to change, but little did I know it at the time. However, this was going to be the start of my last unofficial battle against those who had wanted to see me dead, exactly as Kit had said on her death bed, thirteen years previously, although she only named Peg as the main representative of this intention against me at the time. Now the veil was about to be lifted and the true army of opposition was revealed to me, person by person, day by day.

It all started one day in late spring 1997, when I got a phone call from Peg saying my brother, David, wanted to speak to me. This was an odd request because the last time I had seen him was at Peg's when I gave him my copy of the *Black* album by Prince to hold on to for me. Apart from that we had not properly spoken at any length for thirteen years before this.

All those years ago, he asked me to meet him at the Cowper Arms pub. He sat down with his pint and basically told me that if I continued seeing Dad, it would mean trouble for me, although from whom he didn't say. Then he went on to say it would be best for me and everyone else if I moved away and forgot about my silly music ambitions, insisting that I was wasting my time.

Then, in no uncertain terms, he said, 'It would be best if you vanished for good!'

I took this as a threat that if I didn't vanish there and then, I would be sorry. Apparently, my connection to Dad was making people feel increasingly uneasy, although there was no way I was going to turn against him, not at anyone's request, including David's. He had paid them all with his life for any inappropriateness on his part, and he would never conspire against them even though he had good cause to do so in many ways.

That was in 1984. I didn't take much notice of his brotherly advice at the time, to be honest. I just put it down to the fact that David could not get over the fact of Dad saying that he didn't think he should marry Lyn. The reason Dad said this was because he felt David wasn't ready for marriage at eighteen years old, as he was too young! They married then divorced five years later after having a beautiful son Marc. David had a very strong dislike for Dad after this; he had always been disrespectful to him before, but after this he was much worse. Blaming Dad for his problems was so much easier than dealing with them himself, by taking responsibilities for his own actions and maybe just accepting that he should have considered what Dad had said.

*

The last time David had attacked me was twenty-two years before this moment, but for some unknown reason the situation replayed itself in my mind before I spoke to him on the phone.

I was fifteen years old and it was the hot summer of 1976. I went to Peg's to get some water and David was there with his soon-to-be-wife, Lyn. I got two cups of cold water from the tap, one for me and one for Mark from Tewin Hill. David went ballistic, saying there was a water ban and I shouldn't be using the water. Then he attacked me in a frenzy by first pulling me by the hair to the floor and smashing my head on the table, then dragging me by the hair to the front door where he smashed my head through the front door window. I tried to stop him by grabbing his hands and he smashed my hand through the other window. Luckily, Lyn stopped him and called the ambulance as my hand was bleeding badly. I had to go to hospital and have it stitched.

Just for the record, on the day David and Lyn got married, I didn't go because I wasn't invited, nor was Dad. No surprise there. I would not have gone if I had been invited because Genesis were playing at Knebworth. Phil and Chester just down the road playing drums together; forget about it.

But back to the phone call in the late spring of 1997.

'Sure, give David this land line number,' I said to Peg.

About forty minutes later, David phoned me and came straight to the point.

'Hi, I hope you don't mind, but can I give Colette your number? Because she really wants to speak to you,' he said.

I paused for a second. 'Yes that's okay, I don't mind. Is there anything wrong?' I was very puzzled at this request as it was not what I was expecting to hear at all.

'No, there is nothing wrong. It's just that I saw her and she said she really would like to talk to you. It's nothing to worry about – she isn't sick, or anything like that. She just wants to talk to you because it's been ages, you know...'

I thought it all a bit odd that he was unnecessarily speaking on her behalf and paused again because I found it all a bit confusing.

'... I have not spoken to her in fourteen years – not since 1983, when she said she was getting married. But okay, sure, give her this number and let me know when she wants to talk,' I replied, a bit apprehensively, not knowing exactly what she wanted to talk to me about.

'Okay, will do. And you're doing well and all that, are you?'

'Yes, I am okay thanks, David. You know, I'm working away on this and that. Anyway, lovely to hear from you. Take care, and see you around sometime when I'm over that way, okay?'

'Okay, boss, we can catch up and have a few jars when you're over this way again.'

I thought his invitation oddly over-friendly. 'Okay,' I said and put the phone down. I was a bit confused as to what I was getting myself into. Years ago, I had begged Colette to go out with me for four years from when I was twelve through to sixteen, but she wouldn't. We just wrote letters to each other all the time and I gave up asking in the end, when I met a girl in Tewin called Theresa and forgot all about her. Then after a year or so, Theresa moved on to a more suitable boyfriend. I was working in my first full time job since leaving school in a Fine Fare supermarket warehouse and I went out into town at lunchtimes. That was when a friend of Colette stopped me in town.

'Colette wants to see you because she is not well. She asked me to tell you if I saw you, so can you go and see her?' she said.

I went to see her a few days later. That was when she told me that she thought she was pregnant by some guy she had been seeing and was really worried what her parents were going to say if they found out.

'Have the baby and say it's mine,' I said, and just reassured her as best I could. I told her that I would stay with her if she wanted help. Anyway, she was not pregnant, and we started dating shortly after this situation had passed.

∗

The phone rang; it was Colette. After fourteen years she wanted to speak to me? The conversation went like this:

'Hi, Colette, how are you?'

'Oh, I am okay, I suppose.'

Straight away, this did not sound right.

'Are you sure? David tells me you wanted to speak to me, but he didn't say what it was about.'

'Well, I'm having a few problems with my husband and I'm seeing a marriage guidance counsellor, but my husband won't come with me. I think our marriage is over, but he doesn't,' she said.

'Oh? So your husband won't talk about the problems with a counsellor and you can't get him to go with you?'

'That's right.'

'Listen, I am going to visit soon, so shall we get together for lunch and a chat?' I asked.

'Yes, I could meet you after I have seen the marriage guidance counsellor.' She then told me the time and place of her next appointment and we ended the call at that point.

I drove the hundred odd miles from where I was living, and arrived there early to check things out. I was at the right place and at the right time, but she did not show up. I waited a while, then I went into the building and asked the receptionist if she was there.

Receiving a blunt 'No', I left, a bit disappointed. I went up to Tewin and called her from the phone box. I said that I had been there at the right time and waited, then I had gone inside and asked if she was there, but they said no.

'Who did you ask for?' she asked.

I told her.

'That's my maiden name. I am married now,' she said.

'Oh, okay. Well, shall we meet up tomorrow then?'

She agreed to this and we arranged a time and place. The next day, bang on time, she showed up, got in the car and we drove up to Tewin cricket pitch and then went for a walk. She explained the marriage problems, and I empathised with her as best as I could. Then she asked me about my wife and children.

Taken aback by this, I said, 'What are you talking about? I have never married, and I don't have any children. Who told you this?'

'Oh, it's just what I heard,' she said with a smile and a tone that suggested she did not believe me.

'Look, I can assure you it's not true. Whoever told you this was wrong. I am not married and I don't have any children.'

Anyway, after coming all this way, I wanted to know why she had told David she wanted to see me after all these years. The last thing she had said to me fourteen years ago, just before she got married and I was doing my last ever stint on the streets was, 'Now don't throw yourself under a train, because that would be messy.'

I didn't think it was as funny as she may have done at the time. This was just after I had sent her a card from Knebworth post office. It had a picture of a plane taking off into the sunset with the word, 'Farewell' on the front of it. It should have had a picture of a twenty-three year old down and out in a bus shelter, because that would have been more truthful. As much as I was upset by our breaking up, I knew it was my fault more than hers. It really was the best thing that she ever did for me, even though I did not see it that way at the time.

'So, tell me Colette, what can I do to help?' I asked, with the genuine intention of wanting to help her out.

She hesitated and I could tell she was composing herself to deliver what she had rehearsed before she met me that day.

'We bought a House in Panshanger and can't sell it because we have negative equity on it. I want to split up and get a divorce. He won't agree to this, but if I had the money I could do it and go for a separation,' she said with more business than sadness in her voice.

Now I have never had a home of my own, let alone bought a house. To me, home is where I pay rent or get thrown out – simple, so this negative equity thing was all new to me. However, I very much heard her tone of voice change when she spoke again.

'If I had the money…' she slowed down and implied that I did have the money, by the way she looked at me when she said it.

So, being kind and trying to support an old friend, I asked, "How much money do you need?'

Without any hesitation, 'Fifteen thousand pounds.'

It took me a lot longer to think about it. Then I said, 'I could probably borrow it from the bank, although I have never borrowed money before. The other option is I could ask my friend, who might lend it to me. If I did this for you though, I would like you to come and live near me. I will find you and your son a place to live, then find you a decent job. You could start a new chapter in your life if you really want a separation, and I will support you until you get back on your feet. As far as you and I go though, we can't be in a relationship again; it would have to be just really good friends.' I said all of this to try and offer her a possible solution to her dilemma, that I knew could be achieved. I did not stop to think that this would mean her moving away from her family, to whom she was close.

Her reply indicated that she had not even listened to what I had just offered to do to help her out of this situation.

'Can't you just give me fifteen grand and I will give it back to you, when I have got it? After all, it's not like you can't afford it!' She said it as if I could just pull the cash out of my pocket.

I was confused by her comment. 'What is that supposed to mean?'

Then came the latest story in a long line of untrue, not very nice stories about me that had done the rounds since I had been gone. This was when it all finally fell into place for me.

'I heard that you won the lottery but didn't want anyone to know. Everyone's talking about it, you know. You live in a big house in the country with a recording studio, your kids go to private school. You are married, and have been for quite a few years now…' She spoke as if she really believed what she was saying.

'Stop! Who told you all of this? Because it's not true. I live in a cellar with no windows, under a shop that I rent for a hundred pounds a month. I sleep on a sofa. I have been there almost ten years now. It comes with a toilet and a tiny washbasin that I use to wash in. I work seven days a week looking after mentally and physically disabled people between the ages of eighteen and ninety-six. I give drum instruction at a private boarding school to twenty-two kids, one evening a week. When I am not working, I am writing, playing, or recording. I have seven hundred pounds emergency bail out money for a car, or to find another place to live. I don't have my own recording studio. I have a Tascam 488 multi-track tape machine that's worn out from excessive use and an older Tascam four track tape machine that is also pretty worn out. I use my wages to fund my music and research projects. I don't own a big house in the country; I have no children at private school, or a wife. I know it's not what you may have heard, but it's as true as I am standing here,' I told her, trying to set the record straight.

She looked at me, and I knew her well enough to know that she didn't believe a word of what I had just said. She still thought I was just saying this because I didn't want anyone to know.

'Believe me, Colette if I had won the lottery, the first thing I would have done when we met today, would have been to give you a suitcase with enough cash in it to do whatever you want. The truth is, someone is having a laugh, because it's not true.'

She made her sceptical Colette noises, that she did so well. The bald truth was that she was not interested in me doing anything for her, short of handing over fifteen thousand pounds in cash. Luckily for me, I had forgiven the wounds my childhood sweetheart had left me with, but I had not forgotten. They were not going to be reopened today, especially in such circumstances as these.

✴

I took her back to Panshanger and headed round to see rumour spreading suspect number one, Peg. Now although Peg had married John by this time, I was not told of the marriage until it was all done and dusted. Then, at the start of 1997 she had moved her old mate, Keith Ward, in with them both. John and Keith shared one bedroom, and Peg slept in the other. One minute she made out that it was because Keith was just her mate, and then the next she would be telling me how I was the only one who would understand their 'relationship.' She basically wanted a spare husband, for want of a better way of putting it. Now Peg was married she had a different surname, and she tried to make out to me that she thought that would make it hard for Dad to find her. This was something she would also make out to Keith Ward, to make him all puffed up and protective towards her. She would get off on that sort of thing, even though Dad was no threat to her, apart from being a reminder of the past. John would not buy into any of that, as he knew Dad was only interested in peacefully seeing his kids. The problem with that though was that Peg and Wendy had poisoned their children's relationship with him. Unless he was handing out cash to them, they were not interested. If he was paying out, they became instantly more sociable, and happy to see him. Peg making out that she was worried Dad would find her and just turn up unannounced was not true. The last time she ever saw him was in May 1985 when he knocked on her door to ask where the kids were, and she called the police.

The real reason for her worry was that Keith Ward was living with her, as he had tried unsuccessfully to set Dad up on a drug deal with the police. This was just after Dad had come out of prison in 1974. The planned set-up went seriously wrong for Keith Ward when the police arrested Dad on suspicion of having drugs but couldn't find any on him or in his car. Then, while Dad was being held in the police station he saw and heard the police, purely by chance, giving Keith Ward the third degree about there being no drugs in Dad's car, whereas he had told them there would be. At that point, Dad knew full well what was going on and he was not at all pleased.

*

So, after seeing Colette and having to explain that I was still only a 'nobody,' with fairly empty pockets, I walked into Peg's front room. She was there, doing her impression of a nosy neighbour every time anyone walked past her front window. As normal, she was sitting in her chair, forty fags one side and a cup of tea the other. Keith Ward would always be sitting behind her in the bay window, picking at the scab-infested skin on his arms at his man desk that doubled up as a French dresser… his listening post, if you like, where he would snort his 'marching powders' of an evening when Peg had gone to bed. John would always be in the kitchen to the side of Peg, reading his paper with a fag hanging out of his mouth choosing what horses to bet on at the bookies. That was John's thing, betting on horses; after all, Peg treated him like a servant so he had to have something to look forward to.

After they were married, she said, 'John and I are not physical. He's not my type. We're just good mates and if either one of us dies, the other will be okay.'

Peg was full of unemotional stories like this, then she more or less said that she and Keith were a physical item when she rang me up one day after he first moved in.

'I'm ringing to tell you Keith has moved in with me. I am telling you because you are the only one who will understand.'

'Do what you need to do, Peg,' I said, even though I thought it was a very bad idea. I knew she wouldn't listen to me because she had already moved him in, regardless of what I had to say about it.

Now I was sitting there with Peg and Keith, I suspected both of them of spreading this rumour because it was their style. I waited for her to light up another cigarette and ask John to make her another cup of tea.

'What have you been up to?' she asked, knowing full well I had just seen Colette.

'I have just been to see Colette,' I replied.

'Is she okay? David saw her and said she wanted to see you. I always thought you two would get back together, Keythe, after all, the blokes all like her, she's a very attractive girl. So, what did she want?' Peg knew exactly what she wanted.

'Fifteen thousand pounds and I have no idea why she seems to think I can just give her that amount of money,' I said.

'So what did you say?' Peg said, without a hint of surprise at me telling her this.

I told her exactly what I said to Colette and she kept looking over her shoulder at Keith Ward, then looking back at me.

Once I had their attention, I replied, 'For some reason she seems to think I have won the lottery and I don't know who told her this? But it's not true or I would have given it to her.' I waited for Peg's reaction.

'But you didn't give her it did you?'

'You're not listening, Peg. I don't have it, so how could I give it to her? Do you know who told her this story, Peg?'

She started smiling and I knew it was her. That was why I put her down as my number one suspect, and I was right.

'The way I see it…' Peg began, and I knew this was no small thing Peg had orchestrated here; it was not something that could easily be passed off as just a bad joke. This story had done the rounds with pretty much everyone who knew me down there and no matter what I did or didn't say about it, I would never be believed when I said it was not true. So now Peg was trying to justify spreading this untrue lottery winning story.

'… they all treated you like shit, Keythe. You were living on the streets, eating food out of dustbins, you lost your girlfriend, your job, your drums and your guitars. They stole and sold all your clothes, your instruments, all your records, your photos – they even took all the poems you wrote when you were a young boy. Then when you were starving, living in a bus shelter or in the woods somewhere, did any of them care? No they didn't. David, Maria, Linda, Robert, Lyn, Carol and all the others were having nice holidays, living in nice houses, eating nice food every day. They would not have given you a penny, let alone a cup of bleeding tea. Then years later, you went off and sorted yourself out. Even now they still treat you like shit, they even had the front to sell you photographs and records they stole from you in the first place. They would not give you the shit off their shoe, so why should you give them anything you have got now? Tell me that!'

She said it all as though what she had done was everyone else's fault and not hers. You always knew with Peg she would start justifying her spreading of false rumours with the phrase, 'The way I see it' and she would always end with 'Tell me that!'

So now I had half a confession from Peg and that was her style; she would tell you some of the story but only if she had no other choice. She knew I was not leaving until she told me something, and even then, she never said the actual words… 'Yes, it was me who told everyone you had won the lottery.'

'Peg, I haven't got anything to give them anyway and you should not have told people I won the lottery when you know that is not true,' I said, knowing that this bit of fun was going to cause a lot of silly issues for me with everyone. She was still smiling at this point, and almost bursting into laughter.

'It's not funny, Peg,' I said in no uncertain terms.

'Alright then, but don't give them any money because they wouldn't give it to you if they had it.' She said that just to annoy me.

'How many times do I have to say I haven't got any money, Peg? You are having a laugh!'

I was not laughing and at that point I knew this wasn't over and that even Peg was deluding herself along with everyone else, into believing the lie was true.

*

When I drove away to go back to the music room I was renting in Worcestershire, I had time to reflect on my recent time spent down there in Hertfordshire and what had gone on while I was there. I had thought that people were being a bit odd and over friendly when I had been out visiting, the night before I saw Colette. They were all making out that they were pleased to see me and then seeing how much I would pay for, without letting on that they thought I had won the lottery 'Big time!'

It became very clear when I thought about it and especially with what I now knew from Peg. All in all, those few days cost me almost a month's wages.

It was not the first time Peg had made up stories about me; far from it. There were many stories like: Keythe's married with two kids, living in a big house in the country; he is playing drums for whoever; he is in the SAS; he's in the CIA; he's an undercover policeman; he's in Jamaica with his dad; his dad gave him all the money in the world and now he's living in South America with his grandmother's family. And so on.

Never once did she say he looks after mentally and physically disabled people; he has been a cutting edge key-worker for many years; he washes dishes, cleans floors with a scrubbing brush on his hands and knees; he waits tables in a café; he instructs people how to play basic drums; he supports people in need for free; he has never married; he has no kids; he does not have his own home; he rents but he doesn't live on the streets any more. Not once… and even when they saw the photos and films we had made, they still insisted it was all a front to hide my true wealth. If only that were true, I would have bought all my key people lots of nice things instead of just one or two nice things. It often felt as though people down there never wanted to acknowledge what I did for a living, either because it was not good enough or not what they thought I would have done with my life.

*

This little bit of fun for Peg and Keith got darker and darker and I had a strong feeling it would eventually turn nasty considering the many costly experiences I had endured over the years. After all, now, whenever I visited relatives, they would do things like hiding all their food under their beds before I turned up.

'Cup of tea?' I would ask hopefully, then they would open their food cupboards and fridges and show me with sad faces that they were empty.

'So, you have no milk or teabags? Right let's go to the shops,' I would say.

'But we got no money, Keythe,' they would reply.

They knew full well that I wasn't going to sit there for long without at least a cup of tea. Then, as I drove them to the local supermarket, they would extend the shopping list during the journey to the shop.

'I could really do with a nice fry up, cup of tea and a cigarette,' they would say.

'Okay, consider it done,' I would say. The next thing, I would be at the check-out, paying for a trolley full of food and other products.

'That will be forty-five pounds and twenty pence please,' the check-out person would say.

Expensive milk and teabags, I would be thinking, or I would be visiting another relative somewhere else and there would be a knock on their front door.

'Oh, Keythe, can you get that? I will pay you later,' they would say.

I would answer the door and there would be a person standing there with pizzas.

'Thirty-eight pounds, please,' the delivery person would say.

Later, they would not be able to remember saying they would pay me later.

'Oh yes. Sorry, I forgot. Remind me about it next time you're here and I will give it to you then. I am a bit short at the moment.'

It became a regular thing that I would be expected to pay for various relatives' shopping, costing fifty or sixty pounds every time. If I went into an off-licence it was just the same – they would be asking for excessive amounts of cigarettes and booze and then I would pay. Now most people would say it was my own stupid fault.

'No, I am not paying for it,' is what I should have said and then left them to it. However, I worked for a living so I could afford to help out now and then. It did eventually stop when I paid a debt of forty pounds and a telephone bill of one hundred and seventy-nine pounds, so that my relative could speak with me on the land line. After I had paid the bill, the phone was always dead. I asked her about this and other bills I had paid.

'Tell you what, Keythe, don't call here again!' was her answer and she slammed the door in my face. It was never in my mind that I would ever get anything back and if I did, then it would be a nice surprise, but fine by me. After all, I worked hard for the money I had, and every fifty pounds was a hard day's work.

*

At the start of 2000, a whole three years later, some people still did not believe that I had not won the lottery big time. Anyway, I was incapacitated by a serious Achilles tendon injury at the time. This gave Peg the perfect excuse to visit me at the house where I rented a room, instead of me visiting her.

Peg, John and Keith would turn up as and when they felt like a day in the country. My dog, Boots, would bare his teeth and growl savagely at Keith Ward. He would rarely do this unless he wanted to warn me that he could sense the evil. Peg did bring me some nice videos about Mayan and Aztec history, which was a kind thing to do. None of them could really cope with the fact that I had a few lady friends of mine there, helping me out and caring for me – making sure I had food and whatever else I needed, because I couldn't do much for myself at that time. They were just paying me back for the past help I had given to them, it was that simple. The problem was that Peg, John and Keith all went back to Hertfordshire telling people the house was mine. Then added some colour to the story by saying that I had a cook, cleaner and a personal assistant, and said how obvious it was that I was lying about what I did and didn't have.

When I had returned to normal, a couple of years later, in late 2002, a conversation had taken place with Peg and a group of Keith Ward's extreme far right mates. This conversation was relayed to me by an old friend who knew these people, and he confirmed that the conversation was true.

They were all at Peg's visiting Keith Ward, and I came up in the conversation when one of the blokes said he knew me from years ago.

'Ah, you don't know Keythe like I do. I bet you couldn't kill him?' Peg said as though making an everyday inquiry.

Suddenly, everything that had been going on each time I visited Peg, or anyone down there, began to make sense. Then there was a strange phone call I got from a relative.

'Keythe, if you died, who would be your next of kin? Would it be Peg?' they asked as though I was in an old people's home.

'I am not sure. Why do you want to know that, anyway?'

'Oh, just wondering who it would be,'

Then the penny dropped. They thought if I was dead, Peg would inherit the lottery money, that I never had in the bank. Everything that had happened over the past couple of months suddenly started to make sense to me. Things like being almost run off the road at high speed by a lorry in White Horse Lane; being chased by five or six people in off-road vehicles through the night and then having them chasing me on foot with flashlights in the fields around Tewin; being followed around by various vehicles with blacked-out windows, trying to box me in; someone taking and missing a pot shot at me that hit and smashed a van window in a car park. Then there were the relatives who always asked a lot of odd questions like, 'What car are you driving? Where are you staying? How long for? What time are you leaving?'

Kit was right in what she told me all those years ago, although I did not really want to believe that Peg had set these situations in motion. However, I was about to find out that she actually did. I went to see Peg at her house and confronted her with what she had said to Keith Ward's mates about betting they couldn't kill me. I could tell straight away it was true by the look of shock on her face at being found out – the way she swallowed nervously and went pale when I challenged her. There was also the fact that she did not try to deny it, or even try to lie to me about it, which answered my question. Then she tried to brush it off by half admitting it, trying to make out it was only meant to be a joke and nothing serious. As usual, she tried to turn it on me.

'I don't know why you're getting so upset about it? It was meant as a joke, it wasn't serious,' she said, as though I was over-reacting.

'Well, it is not funny,' I said, but they just didn't acknowledge me. At that point, I knew for sure it wasn't just my imagination; these things were no coincidence. It was true what I had been told and for them, the game was up. Then I went out of the room to use the toilet, leaving Peg and Keith Ward a bit embarrassed and exposed. When I came back into the room, they were whispering to each other and as I opened the door to the living room, they stopped. Then, as though nothing had happened and everything was hunky dory, Peg said there was some bloke a few doors up the road who had a drum kit and he wanted me to pop round to show him how to play it.

'Yeah if you could just show him the basics, go up and see him.' They both said this to each other, thinking that would make me agree to do it.

I had seen the drum kit that had been obviously put on display for me to spot in his front room earlier, when I parked and walked past the house. Then there was a knock on the front door and Peg answered.

'Yeah, yeah – I will send him up to you in a bit.' Then she came back into the room.

'Is everything alright, Peg?' I asked.

'Well, Keythe, if you can just go up there and show him how to play something – it doesn't have to be anything special,' she said eagerly, trying to get me to go.

'Okay,' I replied, 'I will in a bit,' and I could hear their quiet sighs of relief.

Ten minutes later I went up to the house, knocked on the door, and the same guy who was just at Peg's front door answered. He invited me in, showed me the drum kit, and a woman who was there asked me if I wanted a drink.

'No thank you,' I said, sitting at the drum kit. 'If you play a four-four beat along to a record, it is a good way of learning how to play drums in time,' I said, trying to explain.

I got them to play *Like a Rolling Stone* on the CD player – the Rolling Stones version – and then demonstrated how to do it. Ten minutes later, I left and wished them all the best with learning their chosen instrument.

Peg and Keith asked me how it went.

'Fine. I showed him the one, two, three, four,' I said, wondering what their interest was in me going round there.

Then there was another knock at Peg's front door and she went to answer it.

'It's for you,' she said to me, looking rather odd.

I went to the door and it was the guy I had just been demonstrating the drums with.

He held out his hand. 'You dropped this by the drum kit.' He was holding a cling-film wrap with white powder inside.

'No, mate, it's not mine,' I said, firmly and without hesitation.

He then began waffling and tried to insist it was mine.

In my best agitated Michael Caine voice, I repeated, 'Listen! It is not mine. I don't do that kind of thing, never have and never will. Alright?'

'Well, have it anyway,' he said pushing the wrap closer to me.

'No thanks! You have it. Bye!' I then shut the door abruptly in his face.

Peg looked worried when I went back in the living room.

'Is everything all right?' she asked nervously, knowing full well I was not happy with the bloke trying to push powders on me.

'Yes, its fine, Peg,' I replied even though I was annoyed that this move had been tried on me.

'Anyway, you'd best be getting off home if you're going to miss the traffic,' Peg said, changing the subject.

By this time I had a banging headache.

'Oh, Keith has got some really good headache pills; have one of those,' Peg said encouragingly, and nodding towards the drawer where they were kept.

So, very stupidly, and desperate to shift the headache before the long drive back, I said okay and took the pill from him. Then, for some reason, Keith got a road map out and asked me which way I was going back. I told him cross country to the motorway, up to Stratford Upon Avon, then cross country to Malvern.

Then I threw the pill down my throat and washed it down with a glass of water. I lit a cigarette and said farewell. Then I jumped in the car and took off through Old Welwyn, over to Luton, Dunstable, Aylesbury and then on to the motorway. The roads were very clear until I hit the busy motorway traffic forty-five minutes after I left.

It was just getting dark and everyone had their lights on as I eased onto the motorway, then suddenly my eyes started to close as though my eyelids were being pulled down and my arms were being held down by someone behind me. The lights in front of me became just a stream of red and the oncoming headlights on the opposite carriageway were like someone shining blinding lights into my brain.

I thought I was going to crash the car because I was in the middle lane and I couldn't see anything properly. I quickly opened all the windows as I tried to get cold air into the car and I held my left eye open with the thumb of my left hand, while keeping my right hand on the steering wheel. I managed to manoeuvre the car into the slow lane. Through the blur of red and white I could hardly make out what I was seeing in front of me. I could not see the dashboard clearly and had to guess what speed I was doing by how many cars overtook me in the slow lane. It took all the will power I could muster to stop myself letting go of the steering wheel and falling asleep. Then I saw a blue sign for a service station that said twenty-six miles. I concentrated on my breathing and kept on telling myself, 'If you fall asleep now, you are finished.'

The motorway went on and on, it seemed like forever. My eyes were trying so hard to shut that I had to tilt my head backwards and look down my nose, whilst still holding my left eye open. My whole body felt like it was beginning to shut down when suddenly, at last, I saw the service station up ahead. I was fading very fast when I pulled into it. I parked in the first space I could find, clicked my seatbelt undone and immediately passed out, falling to my left onto the passenger seat. It must have been around six p.m. when I reached to the service station, because I had left Peg's at four.

I woke up at eleven forty-five p.m., almost six hours later. Very cautiously but safely, I then drove on to Malvern. At the time, when all this was going on, my mind was set on nothing other than surviving the attempt to cause me fatal harm.

*

The next day, when I woke up, I couldn't remember it very clearly at first and thought it was a bad dream. Then when I remembered it all, I realised that what Keith Ward had actually given me was a strong tranquilliser, not a headache pill, and Peg had said it was really good, but they both knew that was a lie.

Later that day, after trying to understand why they had tried to cause me to have a fatal accident, I was pretty upset because I knew if this situation continued, it was never going to end well. One thing was certain – there was no way I was going to be sent to my grave so easily without a fight, no matter who that fight was with.

I rang Peg about seven p.m. She seemed shocked, and in the absence of an attempt to strike up any kind of conversation with me, I sensed she was disappointed to hear my voice. I didn't say anything about the tranquilliser; I just told her I was fine and had got back safely. Then, without saying so directly, I implied that I knew that the headache pill was a tranquilliser.

Now I was fairly certain that the people who had been chasing me around, trying to run me off the road and shooting at me, all knew each other. They were a gang who all drank at the same pub together. I decided to go and hound them, as they had enjoyed hounding me. I thought I would return the compliment, unannounced, so I trained for a couple of weeks doing Kata, then fighting using the skills I had been taught. I tuned myself up like a machine.

I drove down to David's house early, getting there at five a.m. I looked through his front room window to see him fast asleep on the couch. I hung back till six a.m. then tapped on the window for him to let me in. My excuse for turning up out of the blue was simple enough – I was passing through town and wanted to pick up the tape that Prince's girlfriend had given to me of the *Black* album that runs at the right speed, unlike the bootlegs. I had given this to David to look after for me, although he didn't believe it was the real thing.

He fished it out of a box of tapes he had, because he knew I wasn't going to leave without it. I noticed a mirror with white powder on it and a lump of hash that he quickly moved down the other side of the sofa out of my sight.

Once I had the tape in my pocket, I innocently said, 'Hey,

David, let's go for that drink you were talking about on the phone last time we spoke.'

'It's a bit early for that,' he replied. 'What are you doing here, anyway?'

I told him I had come to see him. 'Let's go round and pick up Robert, then we can go to that local pub you both go to, with your mates,' I said enthusiastically.

He reluctantly agreed to me tagging along with his gang's early Saturday morning to mid-afternoon drinking session, that my friend down there had told me all about.

David was getting edgy at this point because he couldn't inform anyone I was there without me knowing, and could not really say no to the drink, either.

'I'll have a shower and a bit of toast and we can go round and get Robert,' he said, still wondering why I was there.

Eventually, we went round to Robert's. It was nine forty-five a.m. as I pulled up outside his house, which was next door to Kit's old house.

'Now you're not going to start fighting with Robert, are you?' David suddenly nervously blurted out from nowhere.

'No. Why would I do that?' I asked, receiving no answer.

Robert was surprised to see me walking in through the back door, as it was the first time I had ever been there, and I had not seen him for fourteen years. We exchanged pleasantries and chatted for twenty minutes then I took them both to their local pub. When we walked in I could see all the gang were there, around thirty of them in total, even the bloke who had tried to run me off the road with his lorry in White Horse Lane. I got a good enough look at him that day when he stopped at the garage in Woolmer Green immediately after his attempt to run me off the road in his lorry. I had done a U-turn when I watched him go into the garage in my rear-view mirror, and so I drove onto the forecourt behind him, to make sure he knew I had clocked him.

I got David and Robert their drinks, then a fizzy water with ice for myself. David sat with his mates, Robert played pool, and I sat on the far side of the pub on my own, away from everyone. I could see the gang members all looking over at me and then I could see David peeking over at me while he was holding court. Then Robert's son came over with his mate and started asking me stupid questions. I could see David's mates and other gang members all looking at me, but as soon as I looked back at them, they looked away. Robert's son and his mate came over and wanted to ask me questions about where I lived in Worcestershire.

I pulled out six hundred and eighty pounds in twenty pound notes and put it on the table for everyone to see. This immediately held their full attention. Then I put forward my 'fight for money' proposition to Robert's son and his mate to pass round the whole pub.

'How would you or anyone in this pub like to step outside and earn yourself a few quid? Its easy money; all you have to do is come outside to the carpark, then we stand face to face and you can attack me as much as you like. If you can get me on the floor you win, and I pay you. I can defend your attacks, but I can only do three single attack moves on you. If you are still standing and not on the floor after my third single attack move, you win twenty pounds. If not then you owe me nothing, so you lose nothing, and you can have as many goes as you like.'

They did not seem keen.

'It's not dangerous, it's nothing heavy. Just a bit of controlled sparring for money.' I said innocently.

They seemed confused so I explained it again in simple terms, so that they could correctly pass my offer around the pub.

'Tell you what, I will give you twenty pounds each, if you can get me… say, three people in this pub to agree to it, okay?'

They looked at each other, then at the pile of twenty-pound notes, stood up and then proceeded to ask at every table in the pub. I waited over the other side for them to come back with an answer. I could hear them all going quiet while Robert's son and his mate told them of my proposal.

'Keythe, do you want a game of pool?' Robert asked.

'Okay,' I agreed, and went through the motions of playing whilst keeping a close eye on the reaction my proposition was getting.

I played one game and lost because I wasn't there to play pool. I was there to let them know that if they wanted to kill me, then now was their chance. After all, they could have easily overpowered me, robbed me and then killed me because I wouldn't have been able to stop them. The problem they had was they were not sure what stories about me were true. They were not sure if I was this or that, because who in their right mind would do such a thing? I had walked into the heart of their world and challenged them all. As I sat down again, Robert's son and his mate came back over to me.

'Are we going outside, then?' I asked, implying that I was ready.

'No-one wants to know, they all think you have gone mad,' they said, obviously expecting me to react.

'Fair enough,' I said blankly, looking at the gang watching me. Then I stood up and put my money in my pocket. I walked over to Robert and gave him a hug goodbye.

'See you later, I'm off,' I said.

David then asked me for a lift home. 'What was that all about? They all think you're nuts,' he said.

I told him that I was not happy about all the harassment they had been giving me.

'They were only having a laugh, Keythe, there's no need to take it so seriously,' he said as though I should accept that as a reasonable answer in the recent circumstances.

'Oh, I'm not taking it seriously. That's why they are still in the pub drinking and I'm dropping you home now. I just wanted to make sure you all know that if I see you or whoever come near me with your silly threats again, I will make sure you regret it,' I said firmly so that I was very clear about how I felt.

With that said, he got out of the car. 'You can't take a joke. You're out of order, you are,' were his parting words.

'No. I am not but if you or your mates threaten me again, I will be very out of order, okay? Bye.' Then I drove back to Malvern. I knew that what I had done in the pub was not the best way to deal with their attempts to send me to an early grave. However, I was happy that I didn't harm anyone physically, but I did dent their egos. I stood up to the gang's threats and they did not like it one little bit. However, it did put an end to it because the story of that action of mine in the pub did the rounds. I was told the story by my friend down there.

'Oh, guess who turned up and kicked off wanting to fight everyone? Keythe. I heard he had been locked up in the nut house for the last twenty odd years and now he's out, he has completely lost it big time!'

It was all very sad for me, because all I ever wanted were some happy times, but David and Robert were too socially tied to the gang to ever show me any kind of real respect. The very last time I saw David after that visit to his local was when I gave him a lift home from our sister, Linda's, house, late one night.

'Hey David, do you still believe in reincarnation?' I asked to try and see how much he had really changed over the years.

'No. When I die, I am going straight to hell.' He said this without a moment of hesitation, at which point I was thrown by his answer.

It seemed very unlike the David I had known as a teenager, but then that was all a long time ago. I stopped the car outside his house and he kissed me on the cheek, which was odd as he had never done that before.

'Look after yourself, man,' I said, hoping he would understand that I cared for him. He didn't say anything. He just shut the door and walked off down the path to his house. I couldn't understand why he had said that he was going straight to hell. Even after all the bad times he had caused me over the years, I still wished him no bad karma.

On the journey back to Malvern, I wondered if he had done something bad and that's what had made him think that he was going to go to hell. I never got the chance to ask him why he thought that, although I don't think he would ever have told me, anyway.

✳

Around this time in 2003 when I was being hunted and harassed because if I was dead, Peg would inherit my lottery jackpot money that I never had, I decided to call on an old girlfriend of mine, called Eve. Now I had lived with Eve for a while in Stevenage when I had fallen on very hard times. She had been like an angel to me when I was in a very bad way. She loved music in the same way that I did and she taught me a lot about astrology. I had not seen her for twenty years. The last time I had seen her must have been in the winter time when she had given me shelter one snow-filled night in 1984.

When she opened the door to me on this unannounced visit, she screamed and was over the moon to see me. She was exactly the same person I knew all those years ago; very beautiful, full of life, happiness and laughter. I remembered how she would insist I play drums for her in her front room. She loved it and so did I, although I am not sure the neighbours felt the same way. In no time at all, I was dancing round the front room with her mother and her sister who she called round as soon as I walked into her house.

'So, where's the CD of your music then, Keythe?' Eve asked.

The funny thing was, I had about forty different CDs of my music in the cymbal bag I had with me.

'Put your hand in the bag and choose one,' I said.

Eve and her sister took one each. Then Eve started ringing various people up.

'You will never guess who is sitting in my front room!'

A friend of Eve's called Vicky came from across the road to meet me. She seemed to know all about me, but I didn't know her. She said that I was to pop over to her house before I left and told Eve to make sure that I did go over there.

Eve said she was okay, so I went over there later on, when I left Eve's, about mid-evening.

The same thing happened at Vicky's. She started ringing her friends, and a group of girls even did a song and dance in her front room. Lots of different people came to have a chat with me, all being very nice to me and then leaving. They all seemed to know of me, but I had no idea who they were.

It was getting late. 'Listen, I'm going to make a move. Thanks for the tea and everything,' I said.

'Hold on, I have something for you. I want you to promise me you will do something for me?'

'What's that then?'

She gave me three books. 'Read these and tell me what you think of them.'

I took them with me and said I would read them, then I left to go and sleep in my estate car in Tewin. It had all been very pleasant, and no one had asked me for anything. In fact, they had genuinely asked me if I was okay, which was refreshing.

They had no connection to Peg or anyone like that, so I knew they had not heard the 'I bet you couldn't kill him' lottery story.

Anyway, a few days later the weather was so hot, I got myself some water and parked up in Tewin. Over a few days, I read all three books. *The Story of a Child Called It* rang true with me in too many ways. I could relate to the story because I had been called, 'it' by Peg, Wendy and quite a few other people when I was a child. I would respond whenever I heard the name 'it' and I also had quite a few difficult times to deal with, just like the boy called 'it'.

In the story, the boy has a friend who is an older lady called Shirley, who helps him out. Now maybe it was just a coincidence, but the day before I started reading the books, I had started staying on and off with a lady called Shirley, who had also helped me out in a big way when I was younger. She got me an after-school cleaning job, which helped me survive all the problematic times I had as a homeless teenager. Even though I had not seen her for twenty-three years, she was very pleased to see me and insisted I stay with her, so I did stay there for a few weeks. Her sons were a great influence on me as a teenager. They started taking me to my first concerts to see Thin Lizzy, Nazareth, Rod Stewart and Elton John. They had guitars, although none of us could play them, but I got to use them. Most nights after cleaning, I would go to Shirley's house where I would listen to her sons, Stephen's and Gary's, extensive record collection. They had everything from early rock 'n' roll to Pink Floyd. We would listen to everything and drink tea and eat biscuits. Theirs was the house where I really started to understand music as a youngster.

I bought Shirley a big bunch of flowers just to say thank you for being such a wonderful friend to me all those years ago. When she opened the door and saw me for the first time in more than two decades, she just swore in her very broad cockney accent when I handed her the large bunch of flowers.

'You didn't need to do that Keythe, you silly f****r.'

Anyway, it was so nice to see her and she had not really changed. She was still doing a cleaning job after all these years, only now it was for a family in a private house in Tewin and not in a big rivet factory. We had a nice few weeks together.

*

I went back to see Vicky and gave her the books back after I had read them as promised. I have never read anything like them before and found some parts far too familiar for comfort.

Meanwhile, as far as the whole 'Keythe has won the lottery' situation went, I really don't think any of them believed it was not true. About twelve years later, in 2015, I had another call from my aunt inquiring who would inherit my estate.

'Keythe, if you died would everything you have go to Linda because she is your next of kin?' she asked with a hopefulness in her voice.

'No, she is not my next of kin. It would go to my sister, Maria, in Australia, after my friends have had what I have left them.'

This was followed by a sigh on the other end of the phone.

'Oh yeah, I didn't think of that,' she said, totally disappointed.

I honestly think Peg started it all as a bit of fun. It was definitely her idea of a big laugh at first, but people around her believed it was true and took it very seriously. Judging by the seriousness of the most recent phone enquiry, they still do.

I would have thought that by now they would have realised that it is not true. Anyway, even after all the chaos, I wish them all nothing but the best, as I know they would have suffered more than just disappointment if they had succeeded in any of their attempts to end my life. They would have then found out that I really did live most of the time in a small shed with my music and art on the Malvern Hills. Then, more importantly to them, would have been the revelation that I was not as wealthy as the poorest of them. The whole chaotic episode was initiated by Peg saying two things: 'Keythe has won the lottery… I bet you couldn't kill him?' and had lasted from when I first spoke to Colette in 1997 to late 2005 – just over eight years. Then, ten years later, in 2015, I was still getting silly enquiries from wannabe beneficiaries of my death.

This has reinstated the distance between me and some of my relatives, because if money is more important to them than my health and wellbeing, then what else is there left to say?

Chapter Seven

Too Many Sad Farewells

Anyway, getting back to where I was before all of this madness began, I spent the last quarter of 1997 working, then playing hard and finishing *The Lost Chords of Atlantis* CD's, mixing the second CD myself.

I trained hard at Karate to sustain my discipline and good health. In 1998, I worked really hard trying to understand how the Nazca Lines and the drawings worked together. I strongly felt there had to be an answer in the geometry of the whole site; all I needed to do was find it. I spent a lot of time researching the subject online and anything related to any of it, that might help. As a sideline to this, I wrote a lot of classical music and theme tunes, as *The Lost Chords Of Atlantis* had left me a bit lean lyrically. Most of the music I wrote in 1998 was random; there was only an odd collection of songs at the end of the year that did not fit together. One minute I would write a love song, and the next a song about *Stars falling out of the Sky*, then another theme tune. This carried on all year and into 1999. I spent a lot of time hanging out with Nigel over this period. Quite often it would involve travelling off on an adventure to a concert he would be playing somewhere.

One night we ended up in Abbey Road studio two when he was playing the violin parts for *The Doors* CD that Jazz Coleman had put together with an orchestra. Every day was a music day with Nigel and Caleb. It was always a laugh a minute with a pinch of chaos just to add a sense of *whatever next* kind of thing.

*

At work, my Achilles tendon was injured by an electric wheelchair spinning round at great speed. This was in mid-December 1999. Then, on 21 December, I was doing the last training session of the year at Karate when I felt it snap. I stopped training and went back to the house where I was living to put some ice on it. The next morning, the whole tendon was snapped off completely and was halfway up my calf, protruding painfully. I could not walk on it, so I hopped to the landline and reported the injury to my place of work. They refused to pay me sick pay or accept any responsibility for my injury, refusing to accept that the initial rupture had happened in the kitchen at work, just a few days before it snapped. I rang a physiotherapist lady I knew in London. Muriel told me I had two simple choices – an operation or never walk again. So on the morning of 24 December 1999, Dr. O'Dowd cut open my right leg and joined my tendon together again. When I woke up that afternoon, four hours later, I jumped out of bed and showed the nurses that I could walk perfectly well with crutches, but they said I could not leave until eight p.m.

Once the medication from the operation wore off at one a.m. on Christmas morning, I was in agony and it was super painful. Thankfully, I had various friends to help me out with the things I needed while I was incapacitated. On New Year's Eve 1999, I was lying flat on my back with my foot in the air, playing a half-sized electric guitar as the fireworks were going off outside. At the stroke of midnight, I played a song I had written that month – here are the opening words:

You bring me sunshine when all I had was rain,
You set my heart on fire and I can't put out the flames... and so on. I followed that with a few blues tunes, then I went to sleep while the world and his wife were in the middle of the mass celebrations.

I used a lot of painkillers over the next three months, and watched a lot of videos on various ancient civilisations. It was like doing a solid three month course, refreshing my memory on everything ancient, although some of the video's content was debatable. Using a video player with a crutch was easy but changing the video itself was a bit more of a challenge. If I made a wrong move, it was 'pain city' every time. Even though this was a major setback, I was thankful that my Achilles tendon was going to mend. It took three months to walk again, then another six months for my leg muscle to regain its original shape and strength, so drumming was a no-go area for a few months. I used some of the time to listen to old demo tapes, then I made covers and wrote playlists of what was on the cassettes. I also wrote a couple of instrumental tunes.

*

Once I got back to normal in 2001, Nigel offered me a full-time job, so I handed in my notice at my Health and Social Care Activity unit after a twelve-year non-stop run, apart from the three months when I was helplessly incapacitated. Around this time, I had decided to move my worldly goods from the shed into a lady's flat. Thinking it was a good idea at the time and as I had kissed her, she assured me we were having a relationship. What kind of fool am I? I found out shortly afterwards that her so-called 'relationship' with me was just a cover for her real relationship with a local married man. This came to light pretty quickly, the day before I was due to leave England with Nigel to start up his new musical life in Poland. I was in the flat on my own and there was a knock at the door. There on the doorstep was a very sad looking man, who had brought a load of soya milk round for the lady of the flat, who was out at the time. She had told me that there were false rumours about her having an affair with this man, but I could clearly see by the man's face and the way he spoke that this was not the case.

I ignored my thoughts about what I had seen and heard, and didn't mention it. Then I went off to Poland with Nigel. It was great working for him, hearing all the music and learning new things. During this time, I really did not see very much of the lady who had all my possessions in her flat – when I say all, I do mean absolutely everything I owned. – my instruments, recordings, master tapes, songs, books, photos, records and all my clothes. Everything. She started to make it very clear, as did her friends, that she did not like Nigel, although she did not even know him. The fact that I was working all the time and being away a lot got on her nerves because she was not included in any part of it; there was no way she could be. Then she started to ring me on the phone she had given me, saying she did not like me working for him. Over a couple of weeks she became increasingly negative and aggressive about it all. Then I got a call while I was away and, in no uncertain terms, she told me that if I did not quit my job right away, she was going to throw all my stuff out into the car park, for everyone to take what they liked.

I knew by the way she said it that she was serious and would do it; she had been working up to it for a while. Long story short… with regret, I quit my job as she wanted and rang her straight back to make sure she did not go through with her threat.

Once I got back I checked all of my stuff. I didn't say much, although I had to wait a couple of weeks before I could move everything back into the shed at the first opportunity I got. This came when she spent a night at her sister's with the married man.

The next morning, when she came home, I was waiting outside her flat. I then paid her what I owed for the rent, said goodbye and left. She walked into her flat, saw what I had done, and then moved her 'soon to be divorced' lover into the flat later that same day.

*

So, again, no job, but I felt confident I would get one and three months later, I did. In February 2002, I answered a job advert for a person who could play a tuned instrument. It was a job in a local day care centre for young adults with learning difficulties.

I did the interview. They knew me, and I got the job as a Day Centre Officer (level two) who needed to be able to play the piano or guitar. I could almost play both fairly well, 'If you're deaf' as some of my humorous friends would say. So, again I was working in Health and Social Care but now I was in the public sector rather than private. I worked hard to make things happen, although it was all a bit old fashioned and the political correctness was laughable. I have never been fond of the 'We have always done it like that!' culture.

*

A couple of months after I started this job, early in the summer of 2002, the lady from the flat where I'd kept my stuff wanted to speak with me for some reason. I went for a walk with her and her sister on the hills. This was an hour after I had come back from work to find that the vet had been called and my dog, Boots, had been put down in the garden. The other people from the house were burying him in the ground next to the shed when I turned up. I questioned why the vet came and put him down in the garden? I had never heard of that being done by a vet.

During the walk the lady and her sister asked me if I had seventy thousand pounds they could borrow, so that they could take on the mortgage of their family home from their parents. Their parents were about to retire and live in a newly purchased house in France. I stopped at that point, letting them walk on, and I never spoke to either of them again. It was at that point I sat down on the hills and looked out across the vast amounts of summer sun-kissed countryside. I thought to myself that things were bad, not being able to say goodbye to Boots properly. However, if I had borrowed money for them to secure their family home, things would have been much worse, getting myself into massive debt that would have taken me years to pay off.

I carried on working and when 2002 turned into 2003, I had established myself fairly well in my new role as a Day Centre Officer. By the end of the spring, I started having Achilles tendon problems and so I consulted Dr. Brewster in Garden City, who gave me a sick note. I decided to take four months off work to heal myself properly, then I went home to Tewin and Knebworth for the summer. When I was there, I read an Article in *The Times*, where they interviewed Henry Cobbold about Knebworth House. He said in the interview that some Trust would have helped him financially with the massive bills for repairs and restoration of the house if he agreed to certain criteria of the Trust being met. This entailed alterations to the Gargoyles. Henry said he could not agree to censorship of this kind, so no deal could be reached, and he was left wearing what he called the 'Golden Handcuffs'. These came with the job of looking after the estate he had inherited from his family. The article went on to explain that the repairs and restorations would cost many millions of pounds.

'The Golden Handcuffs,' as he put it made me realise that these people who had provided me and millions of other music fans from all over the world with beautiful musical memories did not have endless amounts of wealth. In fact, it was a very difficult situation indeed to keep it all going.

My earliest memory of Henry was some twenty-three years before this, when he had permitted Face to Face (a band I was in) to practice in a building in the grounds of The Knebworth Estate. The guys in the group had insisted that I was going to meet him, and also give him some of my best advice for the future as a way of thanking him for the use of the building. Then they went and brought him into the hall that day with the purpose of introducing him to me. I really didn't think it was a good idea for someone like me to advise a well-educated young man like Henry, but the group insisted I did. So, they introduced us.

'Henry, this is Keythe.'

I was setting my drums up at the time, so I stopped.

'Hello, Henry, nice to meet you, thanks for letting us practice here.'

'And the rest of it, Keythe,' one of the guys in the group said.

'Ah, yes. The advice is, be good to your mum and dad, don't ever get into drugs, and when you meet a girl that you love… marry her,' I said, hoping he wouldn't take offence at my friendly advice.

'And there ends the gospel of Keythe,' one of the guys muttered under his breath.

At the time, I really didn't want to say anything that might change his mind about us playing there, so I made what I said as sensible as I could. A little while after that, we supported The Impossible Dreamers in the barn at the side of the house. That was circa 1980.

*

It was now 2003, so I wanted to see if I could help him raise some money for the house repairs and renovations. So I put some of my songs together and gave them to someone at Knebworth who said they would give them to Robbie Williams and Kelly Osborne. I put a letter inside with a paying in-slip, so that if they wanted to buy the songs, they could pay whatever they thought was fair. I could then split whatever I got between the disabled music group in Malvern and the house.

If only I had thought it through and got someone to speak with them to present this fine idea… someone who knew how to do this, rather than my *Twilight Zone* version of 'how to sell songs in the music business without a representative or publishing deal.' Of course, it didn't work but at least I tried.

It was a record-breaking hot summer in 2003 and I visited many old friends, quite a few of whom I hadn't seen for twenty years or more. I stayed with Shirley for a couple of weeks and spent six weeks in my estate car. Having a car that doubled up as a mobile home worked out well for me because I could move around.

I spent a lot of days in the garden at the back of Knebworth House, writing weird music and working on the Nazca Lines computer idea. Having all these grand ideas was great but there were many times when I just wanted to give up, when the prospect of ever finding anything new and original always seemed to be just out of my reach. That was why I had to go somewhere special; to a place that would not only inspire me to focus on the next step but also had a real magical energy about it. Most days when I was there in the garden, an elderly lady would pass me on her daily walk. Quite often, she would stop to ask me what I was doing today, and I would tell her I was writing or studying.

'Well you have picked a good spot to do it,' she would reply and then continue her walk through the gardens. I looked forward to seeing her; she seemed like a happy, cheerful person and always brightened up my day.

So during the long hot summer days, I would work until I needed to eat, then I would go and have my lunch in the Barn café, at the side of Knebworth House.

The computer program was a long hard slog from start to finish. I began formulating the idea in the garden, and it took me eleven years to work out how it could work.

The other idea I worked on in the garden at Knebworth House, was the Nazca Lines map. If you research the Nazca Lines on the internet, there are a lot of ideas and theories that are often put forward by archaeologists who have spent their research budgets. They then have to come up with something to satisfy their various sponsors. Most accounts are presented as user friendly web pages or 'YouTube' films, composed of holiday snaps or films from the area with a few very well written paragraphs of great ideas. There have been so many great theories on this subject. In many ways, that's what fuelled my desire to truly find something better, that wasn't just another theory, and that I could walk away from and say my discovery was something that would be hard, if not impossible, to beat or reject.

Some of the most recent theories that have been proposed include *The Astrological Calendar*, which was good until it was investigated and then dismissed because only some stars lined up at certain times. *Map of the Stars* is another, although I have not seen any details of this one, other than the theory's title on a list of theories. *Mathematical Message* is again a few words explaining the Lines, with no written theory about exactly what the mathematical message is. Not much to go on. Another claimed it was made by the Water Cult, which may be close because whoever did draw the Lines had put seashells at the ends of a lot of the lines, under various squares of slab-like mounds. The fact that the Nazca Lines is one of the driest places on earth is almost completely opposite to where one might think a water cult might choose to practice their cult ways. I think when they say water cult, they may well be referring to The Sea People, who could be responsible for charting the globe and drawing maps of it. These map-making people are a lot older than our known history of humanity and of map-making. They were making maps of land that has been sunken under the seas for many thousands of years before our recorded history. There is very little written evidence to say where the Sea People were from and so it is still a bit of a mystery. Charles H. Hapgood wrote a book about a lost map-making civilisation, entitled *Maps of the Ancient Sea Kings*. Perhaps this book and a scholar of such a subject may be able to shed some more light on the origins of these ancient people. I have heard that this race of people really did exist and was known to have traded with the Egyptians. However, as I said, the exact details of this would be for a scholar of such matters to confirm or dismiss. This is also often the case with places of mystery when they go through phases where everyone is almost certain that the scholars and archaeologists have it right, then suddenly new evidence comes to light that completely changes all the preconceived ideas.

※

When the summer was over in 2003, I had become more determined and renewed all of my efforts with the Nazca work. I returned to work in the early autumn, where I used any excuse I could find to have pictures of the Nazca Lines at work.

I photocopied the map and gave it to the individuals (the latest label for 'people' with learning difficulties) in the craft group to colour in. They loved doing this because colouring in is a very popular thing within the groups; it is a very competitive activity that has a lot of status attached to it, so it became very much something they were all keen to do. Only Carol, who worked with me when I was based in craft, knew what the Lines were; all the other staff just thought it was the usual colouring activity.

My job was to engage the minds of the people and teach them various skills where possible. This was a very complex procedure; however, I underpinned the engaging of their minds by genuinely making them feel loved and safe. This was mainly achieved by treating them as equals and teaching them how to defend themselves against all sorts of things, in many different ways. This included explaining to them that they had the right to tell someone to go away and leave them alone. They loved this exercise as many of them had suffered abuse at the hands of unsympathetic staff and carers. It was amazing to see how many of them picked up on this teaching and still use it today. They often start laughing when they see me because I taught them how to tell people to go away, in every different way you can imagine! They had been told they couldn't say that sort of thing, even if it was to protect themselves. I explained that the 1974 Human Rights Act from the U.N. entitles a person who is over the age of twenty-one with a disability, the use of the same rights as anyone else.

If that didn't work, they were to tell me, and I would tell their abusers for them. This lesson gave them the kind of 'strength' some staff and carers did not like them to have. You wouldn't think that in this day and age they would still need this kind of help, but they do. We will look back on their unequal treatment in these times with horror one day in the future; of that I am certain.

During my Health and Social Care career, I have saved lives on quite a few occasions. The second of these life-saving times was the worst, when I saved a young man from being boiled alive in a super-hot jacuzzi-type bath. He did end up in the Burns unit in Birmingham Hospital but thankfully he survived and lived for more than twenty years after that. The last time I saw Michael was in a supermarket café in Hereford with his carer when he spotted me queueing up to pay for my cup of tea. He started screaming and laughing pointing at me. Then I had to explain to his carer that we knew each other and had spent twelve years working together, doing many things.

Then there was Andrew who had been given too much medication. It was just lucky, when I got to work early that day and found him on the floor, overdosed and turning blue, that I'd had the right medical training to administer life-saving chest compressions. I immediately insisted that the reluctant staff who were responsible for the overdose call an ambulance, which ultimately saved his life, because there was only so much I could do. The second time I saved his life was when he lay down in front of oncoming traffic, and I dragged him across the road, which almost got us both killed in a road traffic accident. Then I saved Michael again when a staff member forgot to put his wheelchair brakes on and he started rolling off the pathway into oncoming traffic. That was inches away from being fatal. Then myself, a young driver called David and a lady called Victoria saved five people in a flood, when David drove straight into a flash flood river of water. That was when I immediately took over the rescue plan and pulled rank on everyone. I carried three people out of the minibus over my shoulder after lifting them from their wheelchairs. I was swearing my head off at the two staff to keep calm and stay with the people in the bus as I waded through the waist-high water with a person over my shoulder. Then a man on the other side of the river caught my attention.

'Can I help you? I am the vicar of Cradley,' he said.

That was when I stopped swearing and gratefully accepted his help. It took us eight hours to drive the last ten miles home, once a farmer had helped to pull the minibus out of the river and get it working again. Luckily, a teacher who lived close to the flood took us in to dry off. She arranged help for us from some other locals who planned a way back for us across the higher ground.

There were many other times over the years. The last time I saved a person's life was in the summer of 2015, when a young man was playing with his food, pretending to suck a piece of tangerine in and out of his mouth, teasing his staff support member. We were out in the minibus at the time, when suddenly he inhaled at the wrong time and it went horribly wrong. The slice of tangerine stuck in his throat and he started to turn blue. If it had not been for his carer, Helen, noticing straight away, he could have easily choked to death. She very quickly attempted to clear his airway, but was not able to shift it, so I immediately took over, trying three or four times. It still did not work, so I hit him on the back with my forearm as hard as I possibly could, and the tangerine flew out. Now, whenever Russell sees either of us, he wants to hug us because he knows how close he came to dying that day.

People often say to me, 'You must feel good about what you do?' when they talk about my work. Of course, it's always good to save a life; it's not what I would call rewarding, though. It is always a great relief to save someone, especially when you come to think about what has actually happened. I am lucky that I am able to react and do what is required immediately, because some people freeze up in these situations or simply panic. This is something I have seen quite a few times. However, once you get your first few crisis situations out of the way, then that's the hardest part of saving lives done. Then it gets a lot easier, and eventually it becomes more of a natural instinct, just like grabbing someone before they take a tumble.

Christmas 2003 was much the same as any other time for me. I spent the holiday making music, writing new songs and I started doing a complicated chart of angles of the Nazca Lines. This was a bit of a challenge. I spent about two months doing it and once it was done in mid-February, I put it away with the rest of my work on the project.

So, this chart of angles was the start of 2004; then this became my year for experimenting with ideas that people would not consider worth trying. Angles of the Lines was just one of those ideas and the other, more promising, idea was to transfer the west side of the Nazca Lines (half) map on to a map of the world. This map of Lines went from Easter Island to just off the east coast of Japan. The idea was there but the absolute precision was not perfect as my maths skills were a bit below average but as I say, I was experimenting with ideas, all of which took me through the whole year.

In the spring and summer of 2004, I worked hard and played hard doing quite a few gigs with a local blues band. I also recorded a lot of songs I had written and they were okay but I did not send them out to anyone as I would normally do. Instead, I just mixed them onto a CD and put them in my song library. I spent a lot of time this year studying maps and world globes.

I bought a giant globe that featured the flows of the ocean currents. Most of what I was looking at and the question I was considering was: what did the world land mass look like before and after the great flood? Some of this was answered by the book, *Maps of the Ancient Sea Kings* by C. Hapgood. Underwater structures are more familiar now than in 2004 and there have been some very interesting finds in recent years. In the Far East, off the coast of Yonaguni Island, they found massive structures under the water with pathways, steps, and pyramids. Then, off the coast of West India, they found walls and footprints of buildings now submerged beneath the sea. These finds often lead to debates that never resolve themselves and so these discoveries are often dismissed or forgotten.

Most people, though, have at some point or another asked the question, 'Where do we come from?'

There is still evidence somewhere on the planet; evidence that has not yet been destroyed by earth crust displacement or floods. This will eventually prove a very different history of human evolution than the one we live with in our history books today. The history of humanity is a puzzle that is incomplete, with important pieces missing, in my opinion. However, proving that without the actual physical or geological proof is another matter entirely.

By the end of 2004, I was still doing a lot of playing and so my drumming skills meant happy days indeed. Still, working with half a map of the Nazca Lines was hard and to make matters worse, I did not have any idea how much more there really was. I knew very well that what I had was only a small fraction of the thousands of Lines. What I have always worked with is a NASA type version that comes into view when you are above the whole site at a certain height, thousands of feet above the earth. Therefore, only the dominant Lines can be seen and this does not include the drawings of various animals, birds, amphibians or the spaceman. These massive drawings appear as tiny dots on the version I use for my research. This is because if the natives of the area refer to this plateau as being created by the *Sky People* then it should be viewed as they would have seen it, from the sky when they were in the process of creating it. I am fairly sure they would not have stood on the ground to design it, or the natives would refer to them as the *Ground People*.

I was playing drums in The Red Lion on New Year's Eve 2004 and then afterwards, I walked out into the car park, breathed in the 2005 night air, packed my drum kit into the car and looked up at the clear, starry night. For a brief moment, I asked myself if I should release my findings on the Nazca Lines this year? The map across the world idea was nice, but it would not stand up as brilliant. I had an offer to create a website to put the ideas onto. However, when the website was shown to me, it was listed as a joint venture, indicating that the ideas were not solely mine. Forget about it, was what I thought to that – I was not about to hand over the credit of my lifetime's work to someone who had put a few Nazca pictures on a webpage.

*

It was the start of 2005, so I was straight back to work after the Christmas holidays. I began the year by making a few visits to see Peg. I told her in no uncertain terms that I did not appreciate her encouraging people to make attempts to kill me. She still took no notice of me, so whenever these attempts failed, Peg and Keith would make a joke out of it.

'You shouldn't take things so seriously,' they would say.

This situation began to irritate me and so I sat them both down and gave them one final bit of advice.

'You should both be very careful about wishing me harm. You should call off your wannabe hit-men mates. You have had your fun with your 'I bet you can't kill him' game. Now would be good time for you to stop it, because if you don't it may well backfire on you.'

As I told them for one last time, they just looked down their noses at me with frowning disgust. Then looked at each other, rolling their eyeballs.

'Oh, listen to it, giving us the big I am,' they said, laughing as though it was all a big joke.

They did not take one bit of notice of what I had said. Once again, they just dismissed me and continued to talk about all the lottery wealth I didn't have. I spaced my visits further apart and spent a lot more time being highly creative in the shed. I wrote a picture story, *Zero and One*. Then I painted a *Time Travel* picture across the six-feet by eight inches window-sill in the shed. This consisted of the moon on the far left of the painting, a setting sun on the far right and a time travel light in the centre. The backdrop for this picture was a horizontal ocean with the skies above it, going from sunlight on the right to moonlight on the left. This was completed in May 2005. Then I painted an acoustic guitar with a picture of the Malvern Hills with a rainbow going from End Hill across the sky, landing in the River Severn in Upton, by the bridge. This was on the front; then on the back was a map of the world with a sort of Dali twist. I recorded new songs and put them on a CD and then stored them in my music library. I checked the internet on a regular basis for new data on the Nazca Lines, but I did not find much that was new.

My creative instincts took over throughout the year with making music, also. I made some improvement with my piano sight-reading skills, and began to sound a bit better – more so than my usual terrible racket, where I could have given Les Dawson a run for his money. I saved as much of my work and gigs wages as I could. I was getting a bit fed up of not having anything that great to show for all my hard work. I took a lot of photographs of skies and rainbows during the year. I started playing *Texas Holdem* online for play money, and made a couple of friends in America.

This was the time when things slowly started to open up for me. My two new friends were Prism and Playing Cards. We would sit for long periods of time playing cards for fun, then laugh about some of the serious people who were playing as a warm-up for the real money games. Some of the banter was interesting – exchanging cultural differences between America and the UK was an eye opener at times. They introduced me to an American writer called David Comfort, who had secured a book deal with Citadel in New York. He said his book was going to be called *Rock 'n' Roll Book of the Dead* and I quickly became part of his online team of research assistants. David said he was going to be writing about the seven immortals of rock, who were Presley, Lennon, Morrison, Joplin, Cobain, Garcia and Hendrix. I helped him with the Hendrix part of the book, which lasted eighteen months or so. Mostly I checked facts. This was fairly straight forward, as I have read most of the books and have a few well documented diaries of the life and times of Jimi Hendrix, and I used these for cross-referencing.

I did get my Amazon friend, Rich, to check out if the book deal was real, and it was. I did not want to do a whole lot of work free of charge only to find out I was dealing with someone's dream of getting a book deal. David was for real, so I was happy to help. Eventually, I received a large envelope from Santa Rosa, California, in September 2008. Inside the envelope was my signed copy from David Comfort with the words, *To Keythe, Hendrix Scholar and sleuth par Excellence! Rock in Peace, David Comfort.*

On page nine in the list of acknowledgements, my name is mentioned in a printed publication for the first time ever… in an American book. David continues to write books and is now an established writer on many different subjects, including *Improving Your Relationship With Your Dog* and *Publishing*. His success with writing inspired me and we did talk about my desire to write a book on the Nazca Lines back in 2006.

*

Over the past few years I had lost touch with Dad, and so I tried to catch up with him a few times in early 2005, but he was never home when I called. I peeked through the letter box to check he was still living there. One of the times I visited, I noticed his doormat was soaked in paraffin and it smelt very strong. I had a feeling something was not right. I wrote a couple of letters to him, but had no reply. One of the last times I had seen him, was seven years previously, in 1998. He had told me he was expecting a couple of his friends to call, who wanted to speak with me. Anyway, shortly afterwards, there was a knock at the door, and I could tell straight away it was a metal object (a handgun) that struck the other side of the wooden door. Dad said that would be them, and I was to speak with them. I opened the door and there were two Jamaican guys asking to speak to Dad, to see if he was okay. I asked them to wait there while I went and asked him.

'Yes, man! Tell them me rest now, talk later,' Dad said.

I relayed this to them at the front door.

'You have iron? You want iron, me have iron,' the older and smaller one of the two asked me.

'No, I have iron,' I replied, not even giving it a second thought that he was talking about a gun.

They offered me their services, and asked if there was anything they could do for me. Then they asked me, did I need them to go and see anyone?

'No,' I said, 'but thanks for the offer.'

They looked at each other. 'Him like him father eh? Tell Daddy catch him later,' they said.

I said I would and shut the door. Then I went into the bedroom and told Dad that they were going to come back later.

All Dad said was, 'Keat get some food, me go rest now.'

I went into the kitchen and had a lovely bowl of his special soup.

*

The following weekend, I was working in Malvern at the café and I was reading the *Mail on Sunday You* magazine. On the front page was a picture of the small guy at the door, the friend of Dad's I had met last weekend in London. Inside, the article told the story of the little guy who wanted to help me sort any problems out. It turned out that he was wanted on suspicion of being behind the shootings of four people who had been recently shot dead in London, along with untold others across the globe. When I saw the clubs where these shooting had taken place, I recognised them because I had been to them with Dad a few times.

As I was reading the article, I thought to myself that I was talking to this guy last week. Then I realised why he and his mate were laughing when I had said, 'No, me have a whole heap of iron'.

I met a lot of people like this through Dad. He loved to tell them how I played music and worked for a living. They were always amazed at this and would ask me if it was really true. I would say yes, then Dad would laugh at their confusion. Now I know why that was – it was because most of them couldn't understand how I had not followed in my dad's footsteps. Then, 'Is he really your dad?' would be a regular question and when I told them he was, they would be like, 'Wow!'.

The very last time I saw Dad was in the late nineties. We spent a long weekend together. He cooked all my favourite foods that he would always make for me and we shared a few meals with some of his friends. He had taught me how to cook his special soup and other dishes. We had a really nice weekend and were talking over lots of things when suddenly, he changed the subject.

'Keat, me know what you want to know, and I am telling you, I is your father. You must ask Peg who is your mother. You see, Keat, them do it for the money. Me try to free you, whole heap a time. Then them jail we for eleven-teen years! Them is a whole heap a trouble, believe me, boy.'

He said this as though I had asked him to explain things from the past, but I had not requested any such explanation from him. I must say I believed what he told me because as wild as Dad was, he never lied to me; he was never that way with me. Dad respected the fact that I was the only one of his kids from that part of his life that ever took the time to go and be with him. The other children he had, with Wendy and Peg, would never go near him in London without me taking them there and bringing them back. That was Peg's and Wendy's rule for them having contact with him and if anything was to happen, then the police would be called to find me, to explain any problems.

Anyway, the long weekend came to an end. We had eaten lovely food and had quite a few laughs, as normal. I did some drumming for Dad. We talked about a lot of things in a very deep way. As I went to leave, Dad was resting on his bed.

'Well it look like a whole heap a long time me see you again, Keat. You be cool, yeah?' he said as I was leaving.

'I will be cool, Dad. You take care, okay?' and that was the last time I saw him. I think we both knew it was going to be our last time together, but the love we shared would always be in my heart and my laughter.

✳

He died alone, sometime in the early evening of 5 July 2005. I know this because his lady friend who had a key to his flat made a statement. She said she had seen and spoken with him around six p.m. at his flat, then when she called round later that evening at ten p.m. she found him dead in his bed.

At the very same time as he was departing this world, a very strange thing happened to me. The reason I know this is because I made a note of it in my 'creative diary' for that evening. On 5 July 2005, I was in the shed in Malvern. At about eight-thirty p.m. I put my crystal ball in my bag along with my camera. I drove up to the Herefordshire Arms, parked the car and walked up to the top of the Malvern Hills Beacon. I remember feeling as though I was being guided to be there for a certain time before the sun set. I followed these instinctive feelings and made my way quickly up the hill. When I got to the top, there was no one else there. I put my crystal ball into the top of the Ordnance Survey plinth, where it fitted perfectly, as though it was made for it. The sun was just setting in the west and just about to break its last life-giving beam through the light clouds. Then a very slow cloud of mist crept up the side of the hill on the east side of the Beacon like a giant, slow-motion wave. Suddenly the sun hit the crystal ball and cast my shadow, along with the shadow of the plinth, onto the cloud inside a complete rainbow circle. I took a few pictures of this and one of the crystal-ball seated in the top of the plinth.

The photograph of me inside the rainbow circle was published in a 2006 book called *Incredible Illusions* by Al Seckel, Illusions Works – Capella (p.238).

I had these photographs enlarged at a photocopy shop. I am certain they made copies and sent them to the publishers of this book, that is why in the back of the book they did not try to copyright my picture, as I have the negative.

The funny thing was that I would never have known about this being my first ever published work. I found out by pure chance. I was at work one day in 2006, writing risk assessments on the computer. Part of my job was to write then install *Protective Care Measures* for staff to follow when working with people with learning difficulties. These were to be used whenever people were accessing the community.

As I was working, a man walked into the room with a box of books from the book club.

'Where do you want these?' he asked.

'Just put them there on the table, thanks' I replied.

Then he gave me the usual list of books with the corresponding prices. So I stopped typing, put the kettle on, and then looked through the list. I saw that there was a book on illusions. I picked out the book from the box, flicked through it and thought it looked okay. I bought the book and put it in my locker to take home and read later. The rest, as they say, is history.

*

Now, I never knew exactly when Dad had died until many years later, when Wendy's eldest daughter, Lyn, sent me a copy of his death certificate, in late June 2017. She had researched Dad's Family Tree and found this out when she was doing one of those Ancestry DNA things. She could not understand why, although Dad had been born in Jamaica on 14 July 1929, her DNA did not say Jamaica. It came back saying Africa, India, and England.

I explained that even Bob Marley's DNA would not trace back to Jamaica. Even, his DNA would not say he was from there, it would say Africa and Wales. She found this hard to understand, so I tried to explain that more than eighty percent of Americans would be the same and that they do not have ancestors in America. It would be almost everywhere else but not there. It would say Europe, Middle East, Asia, and Africa mostly, but not America.

Anyway, I'd had many feelings that Dad was no longer with us long before this, although to finally see it on paper and to realise that he had passed away into the next world just as I took that rainbow picture on top of the Beacon, was other worldly to me. This got me my first artistic publication and was like a 'sign' to me.

*

I learnt a lot of things from Dad, especially about music and art. He loved those two things more than he loved women and he loved women, but not in a womanising way. He had a wonderful sense of humour and freedom of mind. His cooking was out of this world and filled me like nothing else I have ever had. People would come from all over to eat his food because it was unique, and a lot of it was from his own recipes. People who ate with us treated it as though it was a religious food experience. He was very precise and scientific with his cooking. I loved him as he loved me – unconditionally.

*

Coming back to 2005, I had been seeing a therapist called Sheila for a couple of years to discuss the visions I was getting of losing relatives. Although I did not know Dad had just passed away, I could feel it and kept having dreams about it all the time. Then there were the issues I had been having with Peg, Keith and the army of people they influenced to cause trouble for me. I had explained to Sheila in 2004 that I had been having visions and dreamt that things were going to end badly for those who wanted to cause me harm. I explained to her that I had tried to warn them, but they took no notice of me. Over many sessions, Sheila helped me gain some clear perspective on my situation. I struggled to accept that the dreams and thoughts I had been having kept coming true.

Ever since I was a baby I have had dreams or visions of the future, that seem to manifest sooner or later. Eventually, with her help, I started to think more about my own welfare rather than constantly concerning myself with other people's problems; after all I did that as a job every day. There was nothing I could do for Peg because as hard as I tried to make her see sense, she simply would not listen to me.

Anyway, all the money I paid Sheila for her therapeutic help, she gave back to me in the form of a gift. I finished a session with her one day, and then she and her husband gave me a computer, printer, and speakers complete with music programs. This was worth twice as much as I had paid her for her help. This gift was a turning point for me as I used it to continue writing for David Comfort. I continued to develop friendships online with it and, more importantly, it helped me in my research of the Nazca Lines.

*

So now it was almost the end of the summer 2005. I was exchanging regular emails with David Comfort, helping him with the Hendrix part of his new book, and playing a lot of *Texas Holdem* online for play money. I was working Monday to Friday, nine till five, doing activities such as drama, music, art, craft, computer studies, life skills and community social skills. These activities were all designed by myself and my assistant to engage the minds of people with learning difficulties. Then in my own time I was playing music, writing songs and doing the odd gig here and there.

On 5 October, I rang Peg to wish her a happy birthday and check to see if she got the card I had sent her. We had a brief chat, then she thanked me for the call and card.

At eight p.m. the next day, I had a call from Peg in a very distressed state, saying her son, (my brother) David, had died at home a few hours previously. His common law wife had been out visiting someone at the local hospital and he was at home alone with their four-year-old son when it happened. When his wife returned home from her hospital visit, David was dead on the kitchen floor. Their four-year old son said he had heard David being sick in the bathroom; then he had come downstairs, walked into the kitchen and dropped down dead.

Previous to this, a few months before this tragic loss, Peg had told me that David had lost a lot of weight, going from sixteen stone down to twelve, which raised alarm bells with me. David was part of the very popular drinking and drug scene down there. He wasn't a heavy user of drugs, but he was a bit of a dark horse with all that sort of thing.

I was shocked and felt so sorry for Peg on the phone; no one should have to lose a child in such tragic circumstances. She told me of the harrowing time she had just had, seeing him laid out in the morgue at the QEII Hospital. It had truly broken her heart. I got in my car straight away after I had spoken with her on the phone, with the full intention of going to see her there and to give her my support. I was on the country roads that led to Stratford-upon-Avon and something in my mind urged me to pull over and park, so I did just that. I had this terrible nagging doubt that I was being drawn into this situation without being in possession of the full facts. I felt like I was missing something important that I should know about, so I turned around and drove back to Malvern.

When I got back, I rang Linda, but she didn't know exactly what had happened, other than what Peg had told her. Then I rang Maria in Australia. She said she did not know anything either, other than what I had already been told. I rang round quite a few other people that night and put the feelers out but had no response. No one knew what exactly had happened with David – not even Peg, which I found a bit strange. I did not know it at the time, but this was twelve weeks exactly to the day after Dad had passed away.

Peg came to visit me on 5 November, four weeks after David's passing. She still told me nothing, although I knew she was fully aware of exactly what had happened. I started to worry that she and Keith may have had a hand in the paraffin situation on Dad's doorstep. It would not have surprised me in the least if it had been something to do with them.

Peg started insisting and then demanding that I see a doctor to have a serious health check, in case I was next to die, trying to scare me into action by suggesting that David's death was caused by a heart problem that could be hereditary and nothing to do with drinking, drugs or an unhealthy lifestyle. After a while, I had to sit her down in my shed and tell her in no uncertain terms that I led a healthy lifestyle. I rarely drank alcohol and if I ever did it was minor. I didn't do drugs, except for the occasional *Amber Leaf* tobacco roll up, which I am always trying to give up. I have always eaten healthily, taken regular exercise, and I didn't need a health check to know that I was okay. She then knew I was not going to have any kind of health check.

After a while, I told her, even though I did not want to say it, that if she didn't stop going on about me being next to die, I would take her to the train station and send her home. That stopped her health check requests and her suggestions of me being the next to die. I had known Peg more than forty years at this point and knew that she wasn't telling me the full story. It felt such a shame that she could not tell me, but this was because she knew I wouldn't like the true story. I didn't push her to tell me what had really happened because it would not have been fair on her at that time. My guess was that she wanted to be with me because I was no part of what was really going on. She stayed one night, told me nothing and I took her to the train station the next morning.

∗

I then visited Peg that Christmas, on Boxing day – the first time I had made a Christmas visit in more than thirty years. She sat in her chair in her front room and recounted the whole story about David. She went through the slow, painful details of the night when she had the phone call to say he had died. At the same time that she was recalling this traumatic experience to me Keith Ward was sitting behind her, smirking and rolling his eyes. I found his total lack of empathy very telling indeed because after all, if I had taken the white powder wrap from his mate up the road, it could have easily been me who was dead. While he was pretending to read a magazine in the bay window directly behind her, Peg recalled all the details and turned every so often to look at Keith for confirmation of what she was saying. The whole thing to me seemed incomplete; what she was saying and how she was saying it sounded totally rehearsed. However, I respectfully sat and listened to what she had to say about it. In the end, I still thought there was something vital missing and she wasn't going to tell me.

*

I had not gone to the funeral, as this was something I had never done. My friend, who did attend, asked Peg how she felt about Keith Ward being at the funeral.

'How do you feel about him being here, all things considered?' she asked.

Peg did not answer the question. My friend wanted Peg to tell me exactly what happened, but Peg snubbed her. In the end, I just thought it best if I stayed away from it. I have never attended any of the family funerals; I like to say my farewells in my own way. I can't stand it when people who didn't really like the deceased start saying how great they were. Anyway, not one person has ever told me what really happened with David. This made me think the answer to the question of David's passing was not a good one. I sat talking with Peg for three days and nights over the Christmas holiday, trying to give her some support and hoping she would tell me just what had happened. We talked about everything, except what actually happened to David.

Keith Ward was terribly agitated by my being there that long. He struggled to stay awake unless he was powdering his nose with his drugs whenever Peg was in bed. When he did get too tired, he would go upstairs to bed at five a.m. after trying to probe me for information, double checking to see if Peg had told me anything. Then Peg would get up at five fifteen, when she had heard him go to bed, and start talking to me again. Five minutes later, when he realised she was up and talking to me, he would get out of bed and come back downstairs just to listen in on what we were talking about. That spoke mountains to me because he did not want Peg speaking to me alone.

Anyway, the more Peg poured her grief-stricken heart out to me, the more Keith Ward pulled funny faces behind her back. At times, he sat behind her, shaking his head, implying that Peg was skirting round the truth and avoiding an integral part of the whole story. Peg was not being honest with me, I knew that, but what she was hiding was up to her. I am sure she had her reasons because she knew that telling me was not going to bring her son back.

At this point it was my fourth day there and I really needed a decent night's sleep, which I was not going to get there. Managing forty winks on and off in between conversations, sitting on a chair in Peg's front room was not easy at the best of times. In these circumstances, it was pure endurance. In the end, I had to say I was going to have to make a move. Suddenly, Peg just switched. She stood up as though everything was fine.

'Right, I have got something for you, so just give me a minute then come to my room upstairs.'

She said this out of the blue and then walked purposefully out of the room. So I went to her room, and this was the last time I ever saw Peg alive.

'Sit down and listen. Right, now everything you ever told me about the Pyramids, Nazca, Easter Island and all the rest of it is in this book. Now I want you to promise me you will read it, Keythe, okay?' With that said, she handed me *The Atlantis Blueprint* by Rand Flem-Ath and Colin Wilson.

I thanked her and opened the book to the inside cover of the world map, and placed my forefinger at the top of Alaska.

'I have never told you this, though, Peg. The contour of the west coast of America, starting in Alaska all the way down the forehead of Canada, to the bridge of the nose of southern California, down the nose of Mexico, to the tip of the nose in Panama, then down to the nostrils of Ecuador, on to the lips and mouth of Peru and finally, down the chin to the neck of Chile, looks like the profile of a giant face from space. When you reach the bottom, you arrive at Antarctica, or Adam's apple. This is topped by ice that makes it a circular continent in the shape of an apple with two bites out of it – one on the east and one on the west of South America. These lie either side of the stem of the apple; a stem made of land that once reached the southern tip of Chile. Then look back to the mouth of Peru and listen very carefully as it softly whispers the message it holds from the ancient people of the past to the people of the future. That message is written on the Nazca Lines.'

At that moment, Peg's face beamed with a huge smile. All the stress of losing her eldest son in such tragic circumstances had momentarily lost its grip on her broken heart. It was then that I knew she was never going to tell me what she knew. Perhaps it was to protect me, but I knew Peg well enough to know that it was simply because she wanted to deal with it in her own way. I had to respect her decision, as there was absolutely no point in not doing so. Then, with the unspoken question answered, we both walked downstairs. She put the book in a bag.

'Hide it and don't let them see it downstairs, right,' she said, meaning Keith and John, who were downstairs.

I put the book inside my coat under my left arm, then had a quick cup of tea before leaving. I said goodbye to Peg at the front door and gave her a hug and kiss on the cheek.

Her parting words were, 'Promise me you will read it, Keythe. Look after yourself.'

'Yes, I will read it, promise. Take care Peg, see you later.'

With that, I got in my car and did not look back.

*

Exactly one week later, on 5 January, I was up late watching television. It was well after midnight, and in the room were about forty Christmas cards, all blue-tacked to the wooden frame around the French windows. Suddenly, one of the cards just fell from the window frame in almost slow motion, floating from side to side like a feather would do. As it landed gently on the carpet in the middle of the room right in front of me, I looked at the television clock. It said one twenty-eight a.m. I had a very strong feeling that I should look at the card, to see who it was from. I instinctively knew it was a sign of some kind. I paused for a moment, then picked it up. It read, 'To Keythe, Lots of Love from Mum, Peg, John and Keith'.

It turned out to be a message from the next world, but at that point I only had a feeling it was a sign that something was wrong. I stuck it back on the door frame. Next day, I went to work as normal and when I got back later that day, my Uncle Peter rang to tell me the sad news that Peg had died around one twenty a.m. in the early hours of that day. Cause of death unknown.

I did not attend Peg's funeral. I explained to Uncle Peter that I wanted to say goodbye in my own way. On the day of Peg's funeral, I drove down there, wearing a suit and all that. I knocked on my aunt's door and spoke to her, so that she could witness I was there that day, and then she could tell the others she had seen me that morning. Then I sat outside St. Giles Church, in Codicote and said goodbye in my way, not theirs.

To some, this may seem that I was being uncaring, but I know myself well enough to know that I would have been in a bad mood. I certainly would have happily provoked Keith Ward into a row about the part he played in David's and Peg's deaths, especially if I had got up and said a few words. I would not have pulled my punches or been polite about any of it. Peg would not have wanted that, though. She would have wanted karma and her favourite, *poetic justice*, to deal with him. And it did; almost two years later, on 10 December 2007 I got a phone call at work from my Auntie Ann.

'Happy days, Christmas has come early for you, Keythe!'

'Why is that Ann?' I asked, a bit confused.

'Keith Ward was found dead by John on Peg's front room floor this morning,' she said.

So, finally, after thirty-six years of being the nasty piece of work that he was to me and many others, he was now gone for good.

Peg encouraged him and his bad ways but just didn't see the danger until it was too late. She would have denied that fact. *Keep your friends close and your enemies closer* was what she would have said if she had lived to tell the story.

'Was it drugs?' I asked.

'I can't say, Keythe, but Happy days and Happy Christmas, okay, Darling.'

I rang the local police down there and explained that he had been living in Peg's house so that, if for any reason, the circumstances of his death needed any further investigation, they were to contact me rather than bother John with it. They agreed to this, but I never heard from them after that call.

So, although I had not known that Dad died when he did on 5 July 2005, twelve weeks later, David was dead on 6 October, and twelve weeks after that, on 5 January 2006, Peg was dead.

*

What I had told Sheila during my therapy about my dreams and visions had all come true, although I did not know at the time that it had happened. Now although Peg and I had our disagreements and differences, especially about the company she kept, I could not say I did not love her, even though she poured a large bottle of peroxide over my head, which burnt my scalp and my hair fell out afterwards. She paid me four pounds to admit responsibility for the time she robbed the takings of a bread delivery van of twenty-four pounds, so I had to be told off by her and the van driver, then say how sorry I was and return some of the money that she hadn't spent. I also covered for her a second time by falsely admitting to robbing the electricity meter that she had robbed, and I agreed (on her behalf) to pay the money back weekly to the meter man. At the time, I was too young to be charged and Peg knew it, that's why she got me to admit to her crimes. She burnt my drum stuff and sold all my possessions, or gave most of it away for next to nothing. She then told people I had won the lottery and got people to sell my possessions back to me, years later. She encouraged people to make murderous attempts on my life so that she could inherit the money she knew I didn't have, thinking it was a laugh. I forgave her for all of this and more. There was only one thing that made me think that she would have some really bad karma – she secretly went behind my back and put an end to my relationship with the lady I had good intentions for. I never saw her again after that. Peg never knew that I knew what she and her co-conspirators had done, although it had been relayed back to me. It was pointless trying to get her or her helpers to say sorry. Nothing they could say or do would ever make up for the hurt and sorrow that hateful act left me with.

Peg and Dad had taught me to have an open mind, to keep cool, so I did both, but after this back-stabbing betrayal I found it really hard. Peg would always say things in a philosophical way. She maintained that she believed in karma and poetic justice.

She would do things that she thought were funny, but at the time they were not in any way funny. Now most of it I can laugh about because she had so much front. Unless you pulled her up on the things she did, she would get away with it. When she did get caught out, she would laugh and if you didn't laugh about it with her, she would start a row. Peg loved to start a row about anything. Dad, Peg and I were only ever together on our own on one occasion – in the car, when I was around three years old. Peg said she lost two years that she just could not remember.

'Why question it?' Dad would say. 'We all survived.'

I thought the whole thing had no time to it, but it has been in my mind for my whole life. How do you explain the unexplainable? You don't. You just wait and hope for the best for everyone. One thing all three of us did agree on in our minds was that we never spoke out loud about it. If I ever tried to draw Peg on the subject, she had an answer,

'The way I see it is there are some things you should never question and if you do, then be prepared to hear something you won't want to hear,' is what she would say,

or: 'There are things you know you should say and things you should not, because it could cause a lot of trouble. So, wait until the time is right.'

Dad would be exactly the same, although he would explain it.

'Them no see it, so how them know it true? Keat tell me so, eh?' This would then be followed by Dad doing his best Jamaican rain forest raps where he would condemn the narrow-minded people who stand in the way of other worldly matters.

Then he would tell me stories of the strange people he met on his travels into the jungles of Belize, Guyana and South America. He would say how the women lived by the rivers in such primitive surroundings so much so, that if you lived in a wooden shack like Dad's Uncle did, people would consider you to be upper-class. Then he would find it hard to finish the stories because he would be laughing so much in between his words.

Both Peg and Dad were confident in thinking that as far as that day in the car by the sea went, 'It was absolutely nothing to worry about. Be happy!'

*

John had stayed by Peg's side for the best part of her life. Without him in her life, things would have been a lot harder for all of them and for me. He was a really nice bloke and I could never see what he saw in Peg, but they had a few things in common. They both loved to smoke cigarettes like it was a sport and they loved travelling the world to all the ancient sites. John would finance Peg's incredibly humorous and aggressive thirst to travel. She would almost interrogate people for true answers to the mysteries surrounding all sorts of places – information that was not available to the tourist. In those types of situations, Peg would act as though she had been sent by the Queen of England or the CIA to find out the answers. She certainly wasn't leaving until she got what she had been sent to get. Quite often, she did get the information and other things I had asked her to get. I could not fault her in that department, she did exactly as I asked and got me exactly what I wanted. She would show me the film footage to prove it, on her return. She would always get me a drum from some remote place, out in the desert or wherever it was that she had been. Peg wore the trousers and John paid for them.

One of my favourite films was when she decided to go out into the Sinai Desert, well off the beaten track, with two land rovers. She had six armed giants of men – the sunglasses and suits type bodyguards – for backup who, she said, she had hired, through some tribesman she knew, for a few pounds. Somehow, she was certain this place was real that she had gone to see. It had taken her a few trips over a few years to get directions to this place.

The film location is mainly desert, then suddenly you see this tiny white chapel on its own. They pull up the land rovers like they have come to raid the place. There's a tribesman sitting outside, shaded by the chapel with a very large, old-looking rifle. Peg gets one of the bodyguards to translate for her.

'What is inside the chapel?' is the first question that they ask the guard.

'The Ark of the Covenant,' the man says.

The bodyguard translates this to Peg on film and she is wearing her 'Told you so!' expression.

'Can I go inside and see it?' is the second question.

'No-one is allowed to go inside,' the man answers.

So then Peg gets the bodyguard to confirm with the chapel guard that what's inside is the real thing.

'Yes, it is the real thing,' he tells them.

Peg starts to offer the man all sorts of bribes through the translator, but he says no deal to everything. Then the bodyguards explain to Peg that is as far as they can go with it because the man's job is to shoot anyone who tries to enter the chapel.

After a bit more filming of the surrounding area, which is all desert as far as the eye can see, they reluctantly leave in their vehicles.

A few years afterwards, Peg showed me that film of her at the chapel. The Discovery Channel did a programme about the Ark of the Covenant. They explained that the 'Ark' resides in many religious places across that area, although no one can witness it so it is inconclusive. Then at the end of the programme they concluded by saying that one of the many places it was said to be was there, in the chapel.

Sure enough, it was exactly the same place Peg had visited four years earlier, although it now has a massive metal fence with razor wire all over it, and a heavy, securely locked gate in front of it. The tribesman now sat inside the perimeter of the large razor wire fence, with what looked like a much better semi-automatic rifle.

The voice-over said, 'This chapel in the middle of the desert is said by its owners to contain the real Ark of the Covenant.'

I told Peg about this documentary.

'Tell me about it, Keythe. They didn't put a fence like that round it because it's empty, did they? They just don't want people to know the truth, you see,' she said, as if she already knew about the documentary.

*

So now they have all gone, I have lots of memories and most of them are happy ones. It wasn't the best family life, but it could have been a lot worse. I consider myself to have been very lucky in the unconventional sense of the word.

So even though they are no longer in the physical world, I feel able to make contact with them, for guidance and advice. All I have to do is raid my memory banks and ask, what would they say to this or that? Then my mind's memory bank gives me the answer, even though I may not always agree with it.

Is it wishful thinking or madness? I don't really care. I did exactly the same thing when they were in the physical world and now I do the same when they are in the spirit world. To me, there is little difference. Everybody does it in some form, although there are different levels. These range from saying goodbye at the graveside, right through to knowing you feel a presence of a person even though you cannot see them. It is as though part of their being remains with you in the heart of your soul, a living proof that love is the true almighty.

*

In February 2006, a month after Peg had suddenly died, I took some time off work. I had a break in the Cotswolds for a week and it snowed, so I had very few choices of what to do. I was staying in a coach house on a private estate. Once I had spoken to the owner, I drove to the local shop which was not easy as the snow was getting deeper by the minute. I did my shopping and then returned to the coach house and put it away. I made a cup of tea and sat in the window seat, watching the surrounding countryside slowly disappear beneath a blanket of pure white snow. At this point I allowed myself to relax, safe in the knowledge that I had put myself in a vanished place. The only person who knew of my whereabouts was the travel agent, who had assured me my holiday details would be kept confidential as I had requested. Somehow, being in this position helped me gather my thoughts. Then, during the week, I went out walking around the woodland on the estate in the deep snow, in my green wellies.

I started writing out a list of 'must have this in order to progress'. The holiday break consisted of no television, no computer, no phone and no company. There was just me in a very quiet coach house with a kitchen, a living room with a log fire, bathroom, bedroom and the book that Peg had given me the last time I saw her, *The Atlantis Blueprint*.

She was right; everything I had told her was in the book, although it was written and presented in an educated way. My style is to put things in a simple form, other than when I tend to convey facts and ideas from my never-ending stream of consciousness. That's when it all gets too complicated for even me to fully understand. Apart from all I knew on the subject of history and archaeology, there was much more in the book.

The main beam or band around the world that contained many of the world's ancient sites was new and the part I enjoyed the most, because to me, the sites that didn't land on it were obviously the indicators. One thing I am one hundred percent certain of is that Peg would have known I would reach that conclusion. After all, she was amused but horrified when she came to Tewin to see *Mainbeam & the Indicators* perform. Phil took great joy in dedicating the song we had written about her called, *Oh! Peggy* and the gist of the song was about her being called on to do sexually degrading bedroom duties for a person with an STD.

By the end of the week, I had not quite finished the book as I tended to re-read parts, so that I could fully absorb the information. Trying to understand how I could use this information from the book in my search for progress was challenging because of having to make the decision of its relevance. Keep it or throw it away reading was not easy sometimes. During the next three years I re-read it several times. The fact that the book was called *The Atlantis Blueprint* made me think that Atlantis had been found. However, the book contained new evidence along with the old. One might consider it a masterclass in archaeology and the discoveries found from the past twenty thousand years or so. When I first read it, the thought that kept coming into my mind was that there was only one place in all of the ancient sites of the world that could ever be considered to be a blueprint, and that was the Nazca Lines. It even looked like a blueprint because if you drew the lines in white, then put them on a blue background it would be exactly that. However, doing that did not make it anything other than another blueprint.

The missing, indisputable truth of exactly what it is a blueprint of remains very debatable for the time being. Theories are fairly easy to come up with and there are many. The hit and miss intellectual conference circuit that has been created by mysteries is entertaining and, having so many theories flying around, someone is bound to get lucky and be right at some point.

*

Back to the reality of working for a living in 2006. In March, April and May, someone made three anonymous donations to my workplace. The first was a quantity of maps from all round the world. The second and third were books on ancient archaeology and ancient cultures. None of the people at my workplace wanted any of them so I gave a fair cash donation to the Welfare Fund of my workplace and loaded up my car with the whole lot. Some of it was stuff that I had already read but a lot of it was rare – unique even, and so I learnt new things. This helped me to look at my direction in a new light. It changed a few things on my 'must have' list, that I had made a few months previously. Now I was thinking clearly that I would need something new and outstanding if I was going to be taken seriously, especially in the intellectual world of archaeology.

So, I put my lifestyle into research mode, spending a lot of time reading my new books and then finding out more about their contents on the internet.

All work and no play was not for me so I would relax by playing *Texas Holdem* for play money. I made quite a few millions fairly quickly and enjoyed reading the banter between the players. I kept out of the conversations most of the time as I used it as relaxation as opposed to a night out on the internet. Most of the players were Americans who used the site to warm up before going to play on real money tables. The turnover of players was large, especially at weekends. The funny thing was that some players would get super upset and start saying nasty things to each other – over losing a hand of play money? It's a computer game that is almost certainly fixed in some way within the program. I could see back then that it would become a very popular game, and for a while it made it on to mainstream television here in England, showing live games for big money prizes. It was like watching the games from the Wild West saloons without the hand-guns. Gambling had become huge in England and people were buying into its newly portrayed respectability. For many people, it was the start of a very dangerous and costly addiction.

Anyway, my main friend was an American player called Prism who taught me how to play properly. Prism explained some of the American slang that was used at the tables and I explained to him about certain English slang. Prism and I had been chatting on and off for a year and a half by the middle of 2006. I would often 'give' (meaning 'lose') Prism play money deliberately so that we could play a game. I created the code word 'up' that meant my hand was strong, or my opponent's hand was strong, or that I wanted to get people to bet more because I had the top hand. Prism loved this and it caught on pretty quickly, especially with other players although the code word meant many different things. A bit like when you are in New York and people keep saying, 'Forget about it'. The code of saying 'Up' and its many meanings was hard for some people to grasp. Prism showed me that people play as a team on a table, which I did not know about until I saw it for myself. It was a lot of laughs though, playing cards for fun. During one of our online chats, I explained my frustration because of not being able to find a more complete map of the Nazca Lines. Prism knew about the Lines and recommended various sites for me to check out. I found some interesting things on them.

*

Christmas 2006 came and went. I recorded a few new songs I had been working on over the holiday, but my recording gear was on its last legs and needed replacing. Tascam had mostly gone digital and analogue tape machines had become difficult to get hold of. I much prefer tape to digital as I love the warmth and smoothness.

So I continued to write ideas for new songs but could not do anything great in the recording department for a while. I did try many times to record with my equipment but it was too rough, even for me. Everything sounded like it was underwater and with the tape slipping as well, made it super rough.

Once the new year started in 2007 the *Rock 'n' Roll Book of the Dead* had slowed down to a few questions here and there, until they stopped altogether around the end of March. David said he was going to be finished by the end of the year, so I wished him good luck with it all. Although, it had taken up quite a bit of my time to do the book, I had really enjoyed doing it. The hardest part was to keep my opinions about Hendrix to myself and stick to the story that most people agree with, even though I didn't fully agree with that version of events. It wasn't my book so I only did what was asked of me.

One day in late March, I mentioned again to Prism that I needed to find the best map of the Nazca Lines. Prism knew how rubbish I was with computers and the internet. *Leave it with me* appeared in the chat box from Prism. By early April 2007, Prism had found me the best complete map of the Nazca Lines. I waited at a *Texas*

Holdem play money table for Prism to type in all the information I would need to use to get the map.

'How can I ever repay you?' I asked.

'Two million play money dollars should do it,' Prism replied and so I lost that amount to Prism in one game.

It felt so good after all the years of wondering, to finally have a good version of the complete area. I printed it off straight away and very closely examined the map of 14075 Peru, at long last. I had gone from having about thirty-three percent to ninety-two percent of the Nazca Lines picture at the click of a button, all thanks to Prism. The new version was great and now I just needed it to be enlarged as much as possible, so I went to see the only computer expert I knew, Simon Kitrick, who had given me all the computer gear, and he made it about ten times bigger, up to A1 size. I had twenty-two copies made and went to work on it in a big way.

*

April 2007 soon became a cold November 2007. I heard from David Comfort, who said he was adding the finishing touches to the book and would be in touch. The computer I had been given by Simon and Sheila had been used by a couple of friends of the owner of the house where I rented a room, and had been infected by a virus, which ruined it. I used it one last time to say farewell to Playing Cards and Prism. Then, with regret, I dumped the computer at the tip. The only upside to this loss was that I had learned that computers can take up a lot of your time in a big way, which is not always productive. Today, everywhere you turn, people are constantly using them, although they now call them phones, not computers.

Chapter Eight

The Biggest Artwork in the World

I had performed a few gigs in 2007 and had started saving my wages through the year whenever I possibly could. This was so that I could finance some serious Nazca research.

The idea was to find a place that had real tranquillity, so that I could try and access *The fourth level of super conscious transcendental visions*, as Donovan puts it. I went to Tewin at Christmas, walked around the old lanes and sat in the graveyard of St. Peter's Church. I didn't visit anyone this time, though, which was unusual for me.

After a couple of days hanging around in the Tewin area, I went back to the shed in Malvern. Then I spent the rest of the holiday looking at the enlarged map. I tried and failed to match up the numbers on the map to the list of drawings on the ground.

In the end, I left it for a later date because I needed to be one hundred percent certain that I was right, in order to explain why they were drawn where they were. Instead of trying to work endlessly searching for new information, I decided to approach it from a different angle. Intuition had been the driving force in my life throughout 2007. Now, in 2008, I became super focused. When I was not at my day job, I would either be playing and writing music or studying the big picture of the Nazca Lines.

By late March 2008, I felt I had found the story of the great flood. I recorded that in my research notes and moved on. I began making artistic versions of the map because I was certain it was a multi-dimensional work of art. I gave the first large one to Simon Kitrick (eight years later) because without him enlarging it for me in the first place, I would never have discovered The Starman. I would not have had a computer, either, which would mean no Prism, no picture. Simon did say I would need to go to the Nazca Lines at some stage, in order to be taken seriously, and I saw his point. However, NASA make major discoveries on planets millions of miles away that we happily accept, and they have not been there yet, either… like the face on Mars, for instance. If I went all that way, I would want full access or there would be very little point. What is the difference between going there and a virtual tour? Apart from the cost of a few thousand pounds that I don't have spare, going there just to stand on a platform or fly over certain tourist-designated areas would leave me disappointed as well as broke. In recent years they have introduced many access restrictions on the Nazca Plateau, so there is only a small percentage of it that you can actually visit.

Meanwhile, I felt as though I had to keep my research to myself because I could not clearly explain exactly what it was that I was trying to do. This was because I didn't exactly know what I was aiming for. Besides, whenever I did mention my research, most people's reaction was, 'So what's the point in all of it?' or, what I would most often hear, 'You are wasting your time if you ask me, because it won't change anything.' If I ever reacted to what they had said they would get super negative and start insinuating that I was deluded. This became especially so when I told them that there was no money in it. Instead of trying to explain it all to them, my inner voice would be saying, *What's the point in you? It isn't like there is not enough negative attitudes in the world already.* Then my outer voice would say, 'Oh! Yes, I see your point.' Then they would be happy, because we could change the conversation and deal with whatever was on their agenda.

By this time, I had been working with mentally and physically disabled people for over twenty years and so work was now pretty easy, and very much a second nature thing to me. I was able to keep a lot of my energy in reserve for research in the evenings and at weekends.

I learnt the hard way and kept my own counsel and avoided speaking about my research. Almost three years before this, just after Peg had died, I wrote a 'must have' list, and on it was a research place, where I could make one final push to put everything together. I saved everything I possibly could throughout the year and by October 2008, I found the most idyllic spot within my price range in the Herefordshire countryside. It was way off the beaten track and so I arranged to rent it for one year. It was the sort of place where I would live if I were successful. The fairly small, detached house was split level, with my idea of Paradise for a view. It had a small kitchen, bedroom, drum room, shower, two toilets, front room, and a large, bright conservatory where I could work.

I paid one year's rent up front to the bank. Then I lived off my wages, whilst also paying rent on the room and shed at the house in Malvern. Not the cheapest way of getting things done, but I needed the peace and tranquillity. Now I had a place where I could work safely and concentrate twenty-four seven. So now, whenever I needed to fully get into it and have the work out all over the floor, I could leave it out where it would be undisturbed.

As soon as I arrived there on 1 November 2008, I made a cup of tea, sat down, and looked across the Herefordshire countryside. I knew I was in the right place at the right time, regardless of the financial restrictions this final push of research time had produced. The only people who knew I was there were my Karate instructor, Clifford and his wife Lorna. Clifford came there with me to check it out before I moved in. This helped to convey to the landlord that

I was not to be messed around with and that my work there was strictly private.

I set all the Nazca Lines work up straight away on my first day there. My intention was to start the research the following day. I laid out all the different artistic works in the conservatory, along with the Nazca Lines maps, globes, books, pens, paper and all my various notebooks. There was everything that I had been working on in a technical way for the last eleven years. Also with this were all my internet research notes, along with my hopes and dreams of the last thirty-six years. Everything that was in the room at that moment had made it there for a reason. All I had to do now was prove it. I had everything there that I needed, including a drum kit set up in the other room. I had a keyboard and guitars there so that I could play when I needed to have a break. I had taken three weeks holiday from work so that I could work night and day if I wanted to.

Between 2 November and midnight on 16 November, I finally found what I had been seeking for such a long time. I made my final decision on the stroke of midnight when I walked outside, looked up at the star ocean on the clear blue winter's night and saw a few shooting stars.

It was Saturday 17 November 2008. I was forty-eight years old and for the last thirty-six years, I had been guided to this discovery.

At last, I had found *The Biggest Artwork in the World*.

*

This masterpiece had been waiting to be discovered for thousands of years. I stayed up all night looking at it, then as the sun came up in the morning, I made myself some porridge for breakfast. I stood in the conservatory and looked out across the beautiful Herefordshire countryside, watching the early morning frost melt, as the sun kissed the surrounding fields. I had come a long way from sleeping on the streets and in the woods as a youngster.

Now I was inside, in the warmth afforded to me by the savings I had worked so hard for over the years. Being there felt like heaven to me and worth every penny. The beautiful feeling of having found what I had believed in for so long was priceless after all the painful losses I had endured, always refusing to let it break my spirit. The journey had reached its final destination.

I thought about what I had lost along the way on my journey to get here: a career in music, wealth, success, marriage, love and family. Most people would say it was not worth it and the sacrifices were too great. Believe me, there isn't a day that goes by when I don't think about what I lost for this, but I was driven by something inside that would not let go until I had found the indisputable discovery I had set out to find many years ago.

As I contemplated, a ray of early morning sunlight came streaming through the drum room into the conservatory, and lit up what I had found, *The Biggest Artwork in the World*. There is no known record of this work of art being created and very little is really known about the beings that made this multi-dimensional artwork.

The Ancient quote from the *I Ching Book of Changes* says, 'The history of humanity is written on the face of the earth'. That was the only clue that stuck in my mind as soon as I had read it, and now I know why.

Just like the pyramids across the world which contain many secrets that humanity has yet to find, Nazca, in my opinion, has always been a message from the ancient past to the people of the future. The multi-dimensional artistic nature of the message has been debated for almost one hundred years.

Ancient sites like Nazca, or many of the other mysterious places across the globe, hold fast to their mystery. This is part of the genius of those who created them in the first place. This always leads back to the question, 'Exactly how advanced was humanity before it crawled back from the brink of extinction?'

Judging by the amount of ancient sites worldwide, one would not be laughed out of the room to seriously speculate that the evidence points to a lost civilisation way more advanced than the people of today can truly grasp. If we could try to understand this, then we could decipher the message from the past that would reveal the area code and telephone number to the stars.

Perhaps it may just be that many UFO sightings are in fact ourselves, looking into the past, making various alterations to history now, so that in the future we can exist within the Empyrean and far beyond, in possession of the correct knowledge needed to do so.

✳

For Christmas 2008, I relaxed and stayed in Herefordshire on my own and contemplated my progress. For some reason, I completely forgot to buy any food. There were no shops open on Christmas day and I was hungry. Then I remembered my friend had made me some of her lovely Indian food that I had put in my car, and that was a great relief for me and my stomach. I sat in the conservatory surrounded by all the years and years of work. I ate the small amount of food and drank a few cups of tea with it. Then I played guitar until the farewell sun sank into the ground that Christmas evening. Then I did a bit of stargazing outside for a while before having a nice shower followed by a very peaceful night's sleep.

On Boxing Day, I drove to Tewin in Hertfordshire and spent a couple of days there. It felt good to have got somewhere solid with the Nazca Lines at long last. I went shopping with my Auntie Ann to Stevenage food market and bought some yams, green bananas, chochos, pumpkin and scotch bonnet peppers. These visits would often cost a bit, so I was pleased to get away with just buying her some food and cigarettes; it was cheap at half the price.

On my way back to the house in Herefordshire, I only stopped to get some chicken and flour for the meal I intended to make. As soon as I arrived back there, I felt as though I had accomplished a mission. Then I went straight into the kitchen and made the Jamaican chicken soup that Dad had taught me how to make. I ate really well for the rest of the Christmas period and into the New Year. I had a very peaceful start to 2009, filled with lovely music and food to see in the New Year.

*

In the first four months of 2009 I spent a lot of time looking at what I had found, making sure it was one hundred percent correct and there were no problems with it. There is about eight percent missing from the picture that Prism found for me, but I knew NASA would have it somewhere in their archives. They have the best maps of the world taken from their satellites and spacecrafts. It was just a matter of time (2009-19) until I found the satellite image of that complete area in the public domain. In this type of archaeological research you need patience and a whole lot of determination. By this time, I had been staring at the picture for almost two years solid, in between work, sleep, play and food.

Having made a serious breakthrough at long last, I knew I was going in the right direction. I continued doing my day job, then getting straight back to it in the evening. I decided to make a trace copy on acetate, then use an overhead projector on the wall. The idea was to then put a world map on the wall and see if I could recreate what I had drawn by hand on a map. Unfortunately, this did not work because I needed something much more precise than a cheap second-hand overhead projector. At this point I decided to get all of my globes (some transparent) and study it again with the idea that the artist drew the lines as a map. I had worked with this idea for a few years already. In order for this to work in any way I needed to have a much better grasp of mathematics, combined with an understanding of distances and angles. The first time I had done this I managed to get fifty percent of the lines to run from Easter Island to just off the east coast of Japan. Now, with the rest of the lines I could get them to continue towards New Zealand then across the South Pacific with the ocean currents, then back up to Nazca. At this point, some scholars and historians would be throwing this book on their open fires or log burners before opening another bottle of wine. We have to ask the question: if there ever really was an advanced ancient civilisation, then exactly how advanced were they?

Were they advanced enough to circumnavigate the world across land and sea? What type of Maths did they use… Mercator, Azimuthal, Equidistant or both? In my opinion, whoever drew the eastern part of the Nazca Lines certainly knew pi. If you can see the man standing by the boat which is sailing away from the pyramid with the symbol on it… that symbol looks remarkably like a pi symbol. Their version is so similar to the later Greek version of it. The similarities are so great that they could easily be seen as related.

We should try and consider the similarities between symbols as we do pyramids. They are essentially the same, although they did not use curved lines to draw their version of it. Therefore, it should not be dismissed as just another coincidence.

After all, we as a race of rational beings are quite happy to say that all the pyramid sites in the world were built by people who did not know each other. It is purely a coincidence that they built the same structures all over the world for thousands of years. This explanation of building similarities is what we accept as a historical fact. So surely that would be the case with the symbol of pi? Perhaps the story of Atlantis that was passed on by the Egyptian priests to the Greeks also contained stories of their ancient mathematics? After all, the builders of the Great Pyramids of Giza must have had an advanced knowledge of mathematics and the world before they started building.

We simply say we do not know how they built certain things, rather than say they were more advanced than us or beings from the stars. Progress in such areas as these historical truths are severely hampered, either by political or religious pressures, so as not to upset or change the minds of its followers that rely on its dogma to exist.

*

Through the long hot summer of 2009, I explored every possible way to present my discovery in the most clear and concise way.

By the time November arrived, it was time to return to the shed in Malvern, even though a large part of me wanted to lay claim to my 'brilliant new discovery'.

However, how to do this correctly was the difficulty that I now faced. My time in Herefordshire had come to an end, as had my savings for the research there. Unfortunately, the shed had a large amount of water damage from flash flood downpours. The pitch being wrong on the gutters outside had caused the water to pool and come in through the walls. This had caused about three thousand pounds worth of damage to books and music equipment, so I had a massive clear out, reluctantly taking the damaged stuff to the tip. Then I got a friend to help me change the pitch of the guttering on the outside of the shed so that when it rained heavily, the water went down the hill. This was a big setback and so I put the recent Nazca work away. Instead of continuing with my recent discovery, I moved on to spend the next two years (2009-12) refining the computer idea. In the end, I had a very clear idea of what the program needed to be able to do.

I wrote and recorded some songs in 2010-12. However, these were of poor quality because I had no recording equipment that worked any more so I used cassette tapes. Most of what I have from that time is just one take of sketches of song ideas.

Work became pretty full on and I dealt with it as and when. The time I spent there was either busy doing hands on or busy in my administrative role. I also increased my playing of the piano and electric guitar during music sessions, which were popular with the people I cared for in my day job. I did a fairly steady amount of gigs on the drums, until I developed frozen shoulder in my left arm. This prevented me from doing any kind of energetic playing without suffering pain for days afterwards. It was now the middle of 2013 and this stopped me from playing drums for over twelve months – this after forty odd years of playing without too many problems. I struggled to not let this get me down, when I wasn't busy being in pain. When I became restricted with playing because of having a frozen shoulder, I worked on the ideas for the computer program and what it needed to do to be any good. I needed to find someone who had the right computer programming skills and a high degree of understanding mathematics. The whole idea of the computer program was so that I could present my research on how I thought the Nazca Lines worked as a map of the ancient world. Within this computer program the lines could be enlarged, and the world could shrink so they would be equal to each other. So long as the Lines were at the correct angles and anchor points were in place, it should be seen as a fairly convincing piece of research theory. This would then put the drawings in various places on the globe, like the whale in the sea and the monkey in the rainforest. All that was needed for this was to have the program stretch and enlarge the lines without losing the angles when stretching. This was version one. Version two would show how the lines could be shown as a map of South America. At the same time, the eastern part would tell a story of the people who drew it, and they would be seen crossing the South Atlantic to Africa, on a boat.

The whole idea of the computer program was so that I could present it as a multi-dimensional work, partly mathematical maps and partly the story of a flood. The best part of this artwork is the massive drawing of the Paracas elongated skull, aka *The Biggest Artwork in the World* by J. K. Williams. The quotes I got for making this program were way out of my price range. At which point, I put the notes and work I had done on it away in the shed for the time being.

*

By Christmas of 2013, I was in a lot of pain with my left arm. I could hardly move it from my side and driving was not a good thing, either. I sat with hot water bottles under my arm at every opportunity, to relieve the pain. It felt as if there was a group of people living inside my arm, taking it in turns to dish out pain to me. If only I lived in the future, I could have had a replacement fitted, along with a full head of long blue hair and a six-pack!

I spent the whole Christmas holiday nursing my injury. I had to decline an invitation from one of my best friend's family to a Boxing Day dinner, being in no fit state. It was not a good time; the injury prevented me from doing anything greatly constructive. I had continued to go to work in this condition.

As soon as 2014 began, I got myself booked in with a local

physiotherapist, who treated me with ultra-sound. I had undergone this type of therapy before when, some years after a fall, I had finally decided to get my injured hip fixed. This had been caused from slipping over at work on a spilt milkshake, when working in McDonald's at Peckham in my twenties. That was why I walked out – or should I say, limped out – of that job. It had niggled me for years although I had not done anything about it. Then I heard about ultra-sound, tried it and it worked wonders. This time I did physiotherapy exercises and recovered from the injury six months later.

By July, I was able to play the drums properly again for the first time in over a year. I spent the rest of the summer and into the autumn regaining my muscle memory, playing very slowly and carefully. In some ways the injury helped my drumming skills to develop, because I had to analyse the body mechanics of exactly what I was doing. This led to a greater musical vocabulary, which is always helpful if you are a musician. By late winter of 2014, I was happy to be physically back to normal and injury free and looking forward to Christmas after last year's painfully glum time.

At the beginning of 2015, the health and social care sector was facing some heavy cuts to services. The day centre where I worked as a key worker was to be closed and all staff had to be redeployed to other centres. There was no choice where you were sent unless you were a favoured member of staff by the management, which I was not. This unpopularity had started after coming out as the 'top' of ten key worker officers in a matrix of merit and qualifications two years previously. This led to a lot of complaints and bullying from staff who thought themselves much better than I was. However, the Council had used an independent body to assess each person – therefore you were scored on your sick record, work ethics, performance and skills over the last ten years. It was not based on how much the boss liked you or was intimidated enough to score you higher than you deserved.

I knew there would be little choice in what I got and so I graciously took the job that was first offered to me. I was to remain as a key worker level two but now my work base would be in Pershore rather than Malvern.

*

Before this redeployment, I was physically attacked at work on 9 September by an individual. A member of staff had shouted across a crowded room to him inappropriately and this triggered him to become angry. He then attempted to attack other vulnerable individuals who had repeated what the staff member had shouted.

I safely redirected him verbally to an area away from other people, then he attacked me by jamming me in a door using his full charging weight of sixteen plus stones, which severely injured my collarbone. I left him in the room, hoping he would cool off and requested backup from the member of staff who had caused his anger, telling her to call his carer to collect him. As I was trying to get her to do this, he barged past me, trying to attack vulnerable individuals for the second time. Then, the same member of staff who had been the cause of this violent outburst pulled his coat tails, spinning him directly towards me. Like a shot putter would do with a ball and chain, he came towards me, kicking and punching. After blocking numerous kicks, then punches, I was left with no choice but to struggle to hold his forearms and walk him slowly backwards out of the room to a safe outside area. Once he was safe, the same member of staff barged past me and started a very inappropriate and badly timed conversation with him about his anger. Seeing this as a confrontational issue, he grabbed her by the hair, pulling her head down, and then started clubbing her round the head. Now I had to intervene and rescue her. While I did this, I took many more punches, followed by kicks that damaged my right arm and righthand fingers. Trying to defend staff who are being seriously unprofessional, claiming they were not being intentionally provocative when clearly they were, is always very difficult to prove.

This becomes all the more difficult when the instigator knows you will adhere to your 'duty of care'. To make matters worse, you are not able to use any effective preventative self-defence measures whatsoever in the event of a personal attack. This will, more often than not, end with some kind of injury, as was the case for me in this incident.

I was badly injured and went to hospital to get my fingers taped up, after he had been taken home by his carer. They could not do anything about my collarbone. I reported the incident as an assault on a RIDDOR which is a workplace accident form. This was not filed on the computer as the member of staff who had instigated the whole incident replaced my report with one of her own. Her report did not mention anything about me having to go to hospital, or the injuries I sustained. It just read like a minor thing and very strongly implied that she had successfully dealt with the incident without any problems. This was later confirmed to me by a member of the safeguarding team, whom I spoke to by chance not long after the incident. Nothing of my injuries or of the part that the staff member had played in instigating the violent outburst had been filed in the report they had received.

The attack had left me with a weak right shoulder and a large lump on my left collarbone. I saw my doctor who said there was very little that could be done and that the lump was just a bodily reaction of my collarbone protecting itself. He said the lump would most likely dissipate in the near future.

I spent Christmas 2015 in a lot of pain again. My job that I had done for the last fourteen years was coming to an end in March 2016. I was due to start my redeployment to Pershore in April. Before I started work at the new place, I was checked for bowel cancer, which was not pleasant but the result was good, and ten days after a one hour and fifty minutes operation, I was given the all clear.

*

I started my redeployment job in Pershore at a much smaller unit for ten people who had high needs. Pretty much from the very start I felt the staff team did not like the fact that I was now the third in command, even though I had much more experience and qualifications than any of them, including the manager. They were a 'gang' that had been together forever, and I was not a member; nor did I want to be.

The only people above me were the senior day centre officer and the manager who had made it very clear in an undocumented supervision meeting, that not only did she not like me but neither did some of the 'gang'. She and they felt I was not worthy of my high position. In this first meeting, she told me I was not to speak to certain staff who favoured me. I had been there four weeks at this point. I wanted this meeting documented and she refused to write a true account. In the end, she drafted in a replacement for me and requested that I take a step down to a care assistant post, which is something I have never been. By this time, I was recording our meetings, so that I could write them out on paper. At this time, I had been in my job for fifteen years without any kind of problems like this.

I made sure I was civil and professional after my first meeting with my new manager, although the more popular I became, the angrier she became. Then she told me again that I was not to speak to certain staff. This did not sit well with me; I had been there for just over one year at this point, and things were getting worse.

One afternoon, I was asked to take a young man to the train station to watch the trains, because none of the other staff could be bothered to help him out. So, as normal, I said I would be happy to do it for him. Anyway, we went along to Pershore train station and we were watching trains. The person I was supporting was extremely happy and I was happy for him. There was a young man sitting on the seat next to us at the station, taking notes of the train numbers. I had met him a few weeks ago at an open day at my workplace. I got chatting to him and he told me he was a train enthusiast. I asked him if he had been to university.

'Yes,' he replied.

Then I asked him what type of qualification he had from university.

'Computer Programming.'

After a year of being bullied at work, I felt I was about to get some compensation. So of course my next question was inevitable.

'Do you think you could write a computer program for me if I paid you for your time?'

His reply was instant, and confident. 'Yes.'

I then explained what it was for and what I basically wanted the program to be able to do. He replied that he would draw up a few ways it could be done and get back to me.

'That sounds great to me; speak to you soon, James.' I left at that point and he continued train spotting.

I could not believe my luck, bumping into someone who could actually help me to make progress with the computer program. Anyway, the very next day he wrote me a note with a list of options of the types of maths that could be used. We had a meeting the day after to discuss the options, and decided to use Mercator, as this was the most likely type of maths that a seafaring person would use. I gave him some money and told him to go ahead and start making the program. He accepted the money although he thought it unnecessary at that point. However, I wanted to secure the deal with him. I also gave him the best copy of the Nazca Lines that I had been working with over the past ten years.

By the following month he had made the program exactly as I had asked. He needed to sort out a few final details for it to be a very good representation of what I had designed. It was now May 2017 and James and I had a meeting at my workplace after everyone had gone home, as he lived just across the road. He showed me the way the program worked and then I tried it out, and sure enough it worked. So now there was a way of explaining one of my map versions of the Nazca Lines on a computer. This meant that people could see my theory and decide for themselves. I gave him a final payment and asked him to download it on to a CD for me to use, along with some simple computer idiot proof instructions of how to use it. Then I asked him to let me know as soon as he had it ready for me to collect.

*

My job at Pershore was slowly being taken away from me by my manager and her 'gang'. They had instigated a situation where they threatened that I would have to interview for the job I already had, so they could then give it to their preferred person. Now staff were openly suggesting that I step down to a care assistant post and take a big pay cut so that the young, inexperienced daughter of one of the care staff at Pershore could be given my job.

Anyway, I refused to entertain the idea of doing a repeat interview for the job I had secured fifteen years earlier, or agree with my manager to step down. This resulted in a constant campaign by certain staff, including the manager, to push me out, and so I was unofficially sacked when I got a second frozen shoulder. I had to take sick leave because I could not lift or drive safely. This time, instead of working through the frozen shoulder, the doctor signed me off work in June 2017.

My manager rang me to request a meeting with her and HR. The meeting was just to make it clear to me that she felt I should not have the job, and that I was being unofficially replaced while I was off sick. She then went further and said that I should consider resigning from my job or be redeployed to a lesser role somewhere else. I asked for her requests to be proposed in writing, but she refused. Suddenly, after this meeting, I received a list of complaints from my manager that had been made against me by herself and certain staff.

I answered each one of these complaints and insisted very strongly that they were all untrue. However, if they felt these accounts of me not adhering to my contract or duty of care were true, I would have to insist that these issues be legally investigated. I then sent the same letter of concerns to my manager's boss. Shortly afterwards, my ex-manager and HR came to my home and made a full verbal apology, saying how sorry she was. This was followed by her then telling me in front of the HR person that she was withdrawing all complaints. Again, I asked for this in writing, but the request was ignored, because they did not want me to take things any further.

So by 22 June 2017, aged fifty-six, I was unofficially jobless for the first time in thirty-two years. The council agreed to pay me sick pay and put me on a redeployment list. There were no day centre officer level two jobs available anywhere. The most important thing to me at this point was to get my right arm back in working order, not the job. In my opinion, being in this condition was largely due to the unfair workload that was expected of me after being injured at my job. They were made fully aware of the injuries I had sustained in the Malvern attack before I started working there, but they did not support this fact.

*

After all the years of work and taking only one and a half days sick in the past ten years, I felt very badly treated and should really have taken legal action but decided against this due to there being none of my written accident records filed or records of what had been said to me by management. There was nothing that would support any legal claim of my being bullied, attacked and constructively dismissed, apart from various staff witnesses to the attack. I decided to concentrate on getting my right arm fixed and had a private operation to remove the lump that was beginning to hurt constantly. Not being at work every day was very hard to get used to. The routine of suddenly not being there forced me to seriously think about my working future.

Around the end of June, I collected the computer disk from James with a version of the Nazca program on it. I gave him a last payment of cash and some cream cakes, which by pure coincidence was appropriate as it was his birthday that day.

It felt like my birthday, too, when he gave me the CD, even though the instructions for using it were slightly complicated for me. A computer person would find them straight forward, combined with my instructions of how to place the lines on the globe. The main objective of the program was to show the computer experts a primitive program example, then hope they would say that if I wanted to make this super precise, it could be easily done.

Expensive instead of cheap; Gibson instead of Argos. After all the years of trying to get all of this together, then finally having the map, the story, the computer program and my beautiful discovery of *The Biggest Artwork in the World*, I hit what runners call the wall. It was a case of stop or continue. I was very unprepared for this eventuality. I had never thought about what would I do with it all when I found it. After all, I could not just call up Erich Von Daniken and say I have found something you should see. He and others like him get requests like that most days of the week, I would imagine.

*

This whole adventure had started in 1972 when I first saw Erich Von Daniken's book, *Chariot of the Gods* and the pictures of the Nazca Lines. At the age of eleven. I could not really understand the book, but other people who were older did, and explained parts of it to me. I remember very clearly sitting in a classroom staring out of the window wondering what it all really meant. There was just no way a being from outer space would travel all this way to earth, then need a runway. Erich Von Daniken never said the Lines were landing strips for spaceships…

'… some of the Lines look like landing strips,' is what he said, which is a different thing. However, this misinterpretation of what he said was just someone trying to discredit Erich and his brilliant works. It is lucky this did not stop him opening our minds to the world of infinite possibilities of contact in the past and future.

Between the ages of eleven and eighteen years old, I just touched the surface of knowledge needed to understand the complex world of ancient archaeological history. In the 1970's there was not the availability of information, unlike today with the instant internet library at the click of a button. Back then, you would have to go to the library, search the bookshelves and hope to find something special. Then you would have to consider who wrote it, and whether their historical account was an open and honest one.

There was very little information on the Nazca Lines until the late nineties, when a few well-made maps began to appear. However, they were all incomplete and often mixed up. This is no surprise, due to the very complex nature of the area. If you can imagine a canvas of many square miles that has had many generations of peoples drawing on it, this leaves us with an area of almost a thousand lines or more; then on top of this, many hundreds of drawings. Some were clearer than others, which could be a sign of thousands of years of age. Then you reached the logical conclusion that we were dealing with the works of thousands of artists layered on top of each other. You could call it the original street art. Imagine a Monet painting and a thousand people have a square centimetre to paint on his canvas after he has done his first. This is done over a few hundred or few thousand years. What would that picture look like? Confused, obscured, messy, unreadable, or mysteriously beautiful? The real answer depends on the intention of the original artist. Exactly how good was the artist who came up with the idea in the first place? Perhaps more importantly, before any of these questions can be answered, the key to unlocking the mystery must be found. After all, it is many hundreds of years since the Spanish first documented the Lines. They wrote that the Lines were 'trails' going off in different directions. Then the Lines were rediscovered around 1927 and archaeology scholars have been puzzling over the site ever since. Some have even said that the Nazca Lines will remain a mystery forever.

Numerous books have been written on the Nazca Lines and each has its own merits. I have seriously considered all of the theories that I have read; in many ways, that was how I kept going. My aim was to find something that would be hard, or better still, impossible to dismiss. It took me from September 1972 to November 2008. Thirty-six years and two months was a very long time to search for not only *The Biggest Artwork in the World*, but also the world's most unique work of art. Then spending another seven years and eight months after this discovery working on the computer program, story, maps, and message to the future. Total time spent: forty-four years.

The biggest problem with ancient puzzles is trying to meditate on being of the same mind as the creator of the puzzle, while at the same time remaining rational and focused. If we lose sight of the goal, then we find ourselves making that internet documentary entitled *Mystery Solved!* very prematurely.

Over the years, I have seen a lot of internet documentaries that imply in the title that the search is over, and the mystery is finally solved. I watch them nervously thinking… *Oh well, I tried my best, but they beat me to it. Maybe it's time to do the 'How they built Stonehenge' cartoon instead? Maybe I could do the how the Pyramids of Giza are built on a massive head of a Lion looking East? What about the boy king, Tutankhamen, who was hurriedly buried? He was found in the room outside his mother's final resting place with a last minute wall, made and painted to divide them. That is why the coffin he was found in was pointing the wrong way, because it was not meant for him or that room. It was meant for the larger room through the wall, next door…*

Thankfully, so far, no one has come up with anything that is amazingly out of this world on the Nazca Lines. Nothing to make me stop the process of putting my discoveries forward to the world. My research and discoveries are still one hundred percent new and in my unqualified opinion, indisputable.

✶

So, back to reality: at the end of June 2017 after a daily struggle since I started there, I had finally been bullied out of my Health and Social Care job then forced onto a waiting list for a lowly paid job. It was one of those situations where I had to have legal help or just let it go.

I had received a copy of my Dad's birth and death certificates from my sister, Lyn, in the post and we had spoken about it on the phone, which gave us both some closure. I had more on my mind than work to contend with. It would have been great if I could have shared my discoveries with Peg and Dad because I am sure both of them would have loved it. Of course, this made losing my job seem small and unimportant to me. I decided to occupy my mind and time with better things, instead of wasting my time on the nonsense I was getting from my employers.

*

I was not in the best of physical health again and I was suffering from another frozen shoulder, this time on my right side. It was June 2017 when my doctor signed me off work and my boss had decided to unofficially sack me. I had started spending all of my time in the shed and bought a new foam bed so that I could sleep there. During the end of June and start of July, I began exercising by walking on the Malvern Hills whenever I had the energy to do so. I just could not sleep very well; whenever I turned over, I would constantly wake up in pain.

I started filling my time being artistic – drawing flowers and writing song lyrics. I started to feel as though I needed to stay positive because I knew this injury was going to take a long time to heal.

On 5 July, I drew a picture of an Easter Island statue that also looked like the Pyramids of Giza if you turned it sideways. I stayed up all night doing this and before I knew it, the sun had come up, so I went for an early morning walk on the hills. I packed a rucksack with my Easter Island picture and a compass, then made my way up Happy Valley as the morning sunshine beamed down onto the hill through the gaps in the trees. All I could hear as I made my way up the hill was the sound of the spring water stream running down the hill and birdsong greeting the glorious summer sunshine. It was seven forty a.m. and I thought about how I could improve my situation. I reached the top of the valley and sat on the chair, looking up at the blue, cloudless skies. It was such a beautiful sunny day.

I reflected on my past thirty years, from when I had left London on Monday 12 January 1987 to find a way of writing and recording my own songs. I now had around three hundred songs recorded, that I had written and played. I had them all in a CD library and most of them were written out on sheet music, note for note. Over the many years here, I have learnt to play piano, bass, guitar and drums to a fairly decent standard.

I have learnt to read music and compose various types from classical to rock. This is thanks to my many teachers and friends I have worked with over the years. I never stop learning, that's why I love it. I have learnt Karate and self-defence from the SAS and ex-SAS. I have helped hundreds of people improve their lives, and taught music to over a hundred young people. I have influenced many students to believe in themselves and have helped them to access the power that ignites their own inner talents. I have saved many people's lives. I have protected vulnerable people many times and taught them how to protect themselves. I have learnt how to cook various foods fairly well.

Long gone are the days when I was homeless, although the memory still lingers as it is something I would not want to ever revisit.

At that moment, after resting while I reflected on the positive,

I thought I would walk up to the top of the Beacon. After a few minutes on that long path, a man walked past me with his dog.

'You're going the wrong way,' he said to his dog when his dog began walking with me in the opposite direction.

The tiredness from being awake all night started to set in and so I also turned around and made my way to the much easier 'tired friendly' End Hill instead. When I got there, I found a place to sit, and rested my weary self. Looking out across the lush, green countryside, I felt beautifully inspired.

The idea of publishing the work that I had done on the Nazca Lines began to play on my mind, which was not unusual. I had previously put the Nazca Lines away until I could figure out a way of getting the work published. Most days I would have a moment where I would give it some thought, although I never came to any satisfactory conclusion which, at times, I found frustrating. However, being jobless, it also crossed my mind that I had spent years and years being dedicated to helping people who needed my support. The wages from this work had enabled me to fund my own research, only to now find myself in a less than desirable position work-wise. I could not produce a complete study without access to much better information from Peru. I didn't want to put out a half-baked idea that would get torn to bits by the critics, but I also did not want to waste what I had. However, I felt that the elongated head drawing was the best thing I had ever found and if you turn it upside down, you have the bird, which is also outstanding. I couldn't easily write a book about those two things without a lot more technical information to back it all up. Access to that type of information could only really be achieved with permission from certain departments in the Peruvian Government and the United Nations Educational Scientific and Cultural Organisation World Heritage sites. If I went there, they would not grant me access just because I had made a self-proclaimed breakthrough. They would want solid proof that I had found something worth supporting and I would need help that I don't have, to make that a reality.

There was a recent study carried out by the Yamagata University Group from Japan (2016-18) who claim to have found over one hundred and forty-three new drawings with the help of IBM Japan, on the Nazca plateau, which is an amazing discovery. Some of these new drawings can be seen on their YouTube video, and I look forward to seeing the rest of the drawings they have found. Hopefully, they or other serious parties may consider a collaboration with me to go even further, if they like my discoveries. It was at this point I realised that I needed to seriously think of a realistic way of getting my discoveries out there for the people to see, as I feel I have gone as far as I can on my own in the circumstances.

※

It was around mid-morning when I heard a lady's voice at the bottom of the hill.

'This way, come on!'

It sounded as if she was telling someone they were going the wrong way.

Suddenly, a lady came up the hill with two dogs. As she came closer, I recognised her lovely blonde hair and beauty – it was unmistakeably Kim Wilde. We said 'hello' and started chatting whilst enjoying the view. I thought of the last time we had been talking alone, when we were around seventeen in an off-license in Hartford. This was when we were buying some drink to go to Jane's party. Her friend, Nick, who was driving us there and back, was outside in his two-door grey Anglia car with my then girlfriend, Theresa, waiting for us to come out with drinks for the party. Since then, all those years ago, she had become a worldwide multimillion record-selling success as a singer, touring the world with many other successful recording artists, including Michael Jackson and David Bowie. Her list of achievements in life is massive, including being a Chelsea Flower Show gold medal winner, as well as being an award-winning songwriter, with her rock 'n' roll superstar dad, Marty, and multi-talented musician producer brother, Ricky. We talked about growing food and various other things. It was nice to speak to someone from home after so many years, yet it felt strange to be reminded of the kid I was back then, full of hopes and dreams, all those years ago when we and the other kids would spend our Friday nights at the local youth club. This was held at the same village hall where I had started to play drums and piano in my early teens. I practised there every week and did my first gig there, and then many others later with our band, Mainbeam & the Indicators. A lot of my future started there, though I didn't know it at the time. Kim would be there with her best friend, Claire, queuing up to play table tennis, and I would be there waiting to play another record on the little record player. Those village hall youth club days were the times when I really started to learn how to play drums, so it holds a very special, fun place in my heart. The nicest thing was that after all of her worldwide fame and success, she was still the down to earth, beautiful person she always was when we were young kids.

We walked down to the bottom of the hill and I said farewell. This meeting felt like a very good omen to me. All the memories of being a kid who wanted to achieve something good in life inspired me to find a way to publish the picture of the Paracas Elongated Head.

I felt that publishing what I had 'ready to go' was a case of now or never.

In the summer evenings, I started making various large artistic versions of the Paracas Elongated Head drawing on the Nazca Plateau that I now call *The Starman*. I developed eight versions; each one getting better and better, and that's when I got the idea of writing a story about my whole life journey from a baby to the present. I painfully and critically questioned whether the whole 'discovery' thing was just in my mind or a crazy vanity project. After all, who would really want to read the story of a person who wanted to be a successful drummer/songwriter but failed at every turn yet refused to stop playing even after everyone had metaphorically gone home. A person who could have achieved so much, if only he'd had the brains to find a good manager and conform to the rules. A dreamer who wanted to prove a point, then spent a large part of his life convincing himself, and now wants to convince others that he's right about his so called 'Discovery!'

This story recalls a very large part of my life journey, all the ups and downs that were at times sad, but thankfully I survived. I have used negative and positive times as a vehicle to get the picture out there into the public domain. From this position, I can now finally make claim to my unique discovery before others try to claim it as their own or use it without crediting me.

*

The age of the Paracas people who have been found in and around Nazca with their elongated heads is still debatable, as are their beliefs and skills. The area that surrounds the Nazca Plateau has an underwater irrigation system that is thousands of years old. This supplies the surrounding fields with fresh water that has run through the sands to be purified. If you look carefully at the satellite image of the area and follow the irrigated fields around the plateau, they define the shape of the Paracas Elongated Head.

Some experts say the Paracas were a peaceful race of beings that may have either been wiped out by war or died out then replaced by the Nazca Indians. There is a South American Indian legend that a race of advanced people came from the sea and landed on the coast of Peru thousands of years ago, sometime after the great flood. Historians say this refers to Viracocha from the Inca mythology, who they considered to be the creator of all things and who is strongly connected to the sea. There are no records anywhere else in the world to say where they came from. This leads me to believe the answer to that question is yet to be found.

However, if this advanced race of people came from the land mass which is now the South Pole, a place that has recently been shown to have had more clement weather and vegetation before the volcanoes erupted, then possibly this triggered the migration to South America, and it would explain their unknown origins. Massive lava flows of a superheated nature under the ice sheet would have caused a very fast, massive rise in sea level across the world. These volcanic eruptions could have then been rapidly followed by massive ice sheets sliding into the sea, causing Tsunamis across the planet. This would explain the cause of what is known as the great flood wiping out coastal communities first, then moving inland across the globe. Once the volcanoes cooled again, the ice sheets at the North and South Poles had both moved, after melting then refreezing. Scientific research has found proof that the same volcanic ash can be found at the North and South Poles, indicating there was a massive eruption that covered the whole planet in ash. This may explain why many humans who survived, lived underground thousands of years ago. This could be due to the inhospitable air quality the eruptions had caused after the great flood had retreated to the oceans of today. However, I strongly believe the humans who made the worldwide underground dwellings after the flood were also avoiding prehistoric predators for many years. Once this part of the ancient cataclysm was over, the North Pole had moved from the land in North America and Canada into the sea. The southern ice cap moved from the Indian Ocean onto the land of the South Pole, covering the mythical land that some claim to be Atlantis. This change of Pole positions would explain ancient maps of an ice-free South Pole and recent scientific research that claims it was once ice-free.

*

Over the past forty-four years, I have searched outside of myself and deep inside my mind until I found what the Sky People from the ancient Peruvian site of Nazca had left for us… *The Biggest Artwork in the World*. When I had finally found it, the Ancient Chinese I Ching quote made perfect sense: *The history of humanity is written on the face of the earth.*

Nazca is a massive drawing of a Paracas face with an elongated head that can only really be seen from space. It is looking at its home, which is starting to push through the melting ice at the South Pole.

79○58'39.25"/81○57'32.21"0